£3·80
R

· PASSPORT ·
TO

ARABIA

Passport is published by:
Passport, 5 Parsonage Street, Wistow, Huntingdon, Cambs PE17 2QD
in conjunction with
Serpent's Tail, 4 Blackstock Mews, London N4 2BT

Editors: Mike Gerrard, Thomas McCarthy

All manuscripts are welcome but must be accompanied by a
stamped addressed envelope or they cannot be returned.
Collections of stories cannot be considered without the
prior agreement of the Editors.

Published with the assistance of the Eastern Arts Association

Serpent's Tail ISBN 1-85242-345-5
Passport ISBN 1-897779-00-3
A CIP catalogue record for this book is available from the British Library

Passport is printed by Antony Rowe Ltd, Chippenham, Wilts

PASSPORT TO ARABIA

CONTENTS

ARABIA:

Passport 1

First world publication of Ivan Klima's banned story, "The Firebug"

Julian Critchley on
The Backbench Bazaar
(*The Daily Telegraph* on Julian Critchley:
"Anyone who can say of Dennis Skinner,
'he would not hurt a fly unless it were
stationary' surely deserves Junior
Minister status at least.")

An interview with Martha Gellhorn
("One of the best-respected war
correspondents of the century":
The Sunday Times)

An extract from *Behind the Waterfall*
by Chinatsu Nakayama
("Universally entertaining stories and a
fresh eye on modern Japan":
The Observer
"...a crackling sense of humour...the
funniest story I've read about television....
a stellar debut"
Marianne Wiggins in *The Sunday Times*)

A short story from Juan Jose Saer
("I can't understand why ... we have had
to wait so long for a book of his to
appear in English"
The Independent on Sunday on
Juan Jose Saer's novel, *The Witness*)

I. van Mil
HEAVENS!

Reverend Adams would gaze at the leather-clad girls in their short zippered skirts, latticed stockings and black creaking jackets studded with galaxies of stainless steel stars. At inconvenient moments his mind would pause over high buckled boots, armoured hips, leopard bosoms and frescoed faces. He yearned to finger lacquered rainbow tresses, to lose himself in harlequin eyes. "Angel mammas," he would sigh, then sternly remind himself that he had chosen a different orbit. But they would filter back in cigarette mists blown from white or blue or sunset smiles and meander, chains swaying, rivets gleaming, through his defeated reveries. He was uneasy about these waverings and tried to tame his meditations by charting the theological mazes which had disciplined aeons of saintly sages. But he was too eager for life to follow their dry thorny intricacies. The most obvious religious dilemma reared its horns - How many angels can dance on the head of a pin? - and impaled him on visions of polished steel safety pins spangling the night sky, on their clasps an infinity of jack-booted Hell's Angel mammas gyrating to the sphere-shattering rhythms of a celestial heavy metal band.

Freewheeling Frank Adams, as he was then, had misspent his youth astride a monster motorcycle, a painted peroxided girl clutching his leather back, part of a chrome and black cavalcade roaring along the high summer roads of paradise. Traffic would pull aside to let the outlaw convoy through. Police were outnumbered and could only provide a kind of escort as it stormed towards tense seaside towns, the unwilling Bank Holiday valhallas, where blood and beer and girls would flow in the heat and glare of a driftwood inferno. The discontent had snaked into his mindless zeal, a squirming suspicion that 1000cc of immaculately-tuned metal was not the ultimate measure of things, that there is more to love than the feeling you get when you value someone as much as your bike. He hesitated at a junction. The cortege reeled on its way but he slowed and, not without regret, turned away. Glancing in his rear-view mirror he saw the girl waiting at the crossroads.

A clerical collar soon covered the tattoos on his neck, and his motorcycle conveyed him on parish rounds. But his aspirations soared, no longer limited by the world he had warred against. However, the Eden drug lingered in his veins and he would catch himself gazing at the girls or full-throttling along the open road with windscream in his ears and tears streaming from wind-burned eyeballs. It was not that he found no satisfaction after the forbidden tasting. On the contrary, he was routinely acceptably content. But compared to the ecstasies of those golden days before the ripening fruit had tempted him with its lush divine promise, it was mundane.

"I have this problem," he confessed to his spiritual consultant.

"Problems are opportunities," was the brisk confident reply. His superior, an upwardly-mobile career clergyman who studied business management techniques, saw himself as a main board director of a multi-million pound multi-national conglomerate preparing a take-over bid. He adjusted his designer spectacles and inspected his multi-function watch.

"Where there's a problem, there's a solution. Break it down into sub-problems and deal with them separately. There's only one competitor for our market sector but he's fierce, he's cunning, and all problems eventually boil down to him. Ask yourself why he's expending his resources on you. I reckon it's because he knows we've got the edge on him. If I were you, I'd get in there and flush out the wildlife."

Reverend Adams was impressed by this advice. "He'll go far," he thought. "I could do worse than cruise in his slip-stream."

"This could be a whole new field of operation for us. Remember not to lose sight of the needs of the customers. Meet them on their own terms and then consider how we can trim our product to suit. The trick is to look into the whites of their eyes at

6

the crucial moment and come up with the best deal, the one they can't refuse. The competition won't get a look-in. It's a win or lose situation. Shoot straight from the hip."

Reverend Adams hesitated, seeking an appropriate phrase. "I would say our competitor had already established a strong presence."

"No one said it would be a piece of cake," and with a final glance at his watch he went back to his computerised market projections and forward planning strategies.

Reverend Adams no longer washed or shaved. Over his clerical collar he donned musty Hell's Angel colours - the soiled and tattered denim originals of his initiation, the fringed jacket emblazoned with the winged and helmeted skull. He wiped engine grease into his hair as he overhauled his motorcycle to respond to every whim change. By day its oriental scream seared through the parish. At night he bundled his clothes under the crank-case to absorb any stray oily drips.

Before long, motorcycles leaned in front of the church. The congregation, after an initial increase to verify with its own eyes the hardly-to-be-believed rumours, did not so much dwindle as evacuate to a neighbouring parish for the duration of the crisis. Each Sunday morning the piles of helmets, chains, axes and crowbars grew larger in the porch as more and more bikers came to hear the sermons which drew heavily on angelic allusions from the Bible. Social events in the hall turned into meetings of the local Hell's Angel Chapter. The Friday junior disco became the gathering place for swaggering Angel children, and Reverend Adams took a special interest in the activities of the renamed Mammas' Union. As dark murmurings spread against him, he tried to explain to the troubled Parochial Church Council, "Their vow is to be righteous Angels. I'm helping to do just that." The PCC voted by a small majority to adopt a short-term wait-and-see policy. Where charity prevailed he was given credit for his canny ability to relate to the outlaws, meeting them on their own terms without, so far, seeming to compromise his own, and perhaps, who knows, broadening the scope of the fold. Even though those already in the fold were horrified by the new recruits. Indeed, he related so well that the police asked him to help with some of their enquiries.

"I think we're on to something big!" he reported excitedly to his spiritual consultant.

His superior was more cautious. "Don't count your chickens yet but keep the heat on. And keep your eyes peeled for the right moment before you move in for the kill."

Reverend Adams thought carefully before replying, "I would prefer to make it sooner rather than later. The established customers have started voting with their feet."

The spiritual consultant paused. he removed his spectacles, breathed on the lenses and polished them with a mauve handkerchief. Things were careering out of control, he thought. Whereas he would prefer a softly-softly approach, playing the quarry until there was no remaining doubt about which way the balance would tip, Reverend Adams had all the finesse of a stampede in a china shop. On the other hand, he reflected, the cruder methods were sometimes the most effective way to beat off the competition. Absently pushing the entire sequence of functions on his watch, he weighed the likelihood of the project coming off, and the kudos that would bring, against his wish to remain well outside the trajectory of any substance hitting the proverbial fan. He decided to distance himself. "Well," he said, "it's your deal. Keep your cool or the whole thing will be too hot to handle."

So Reverend Adams continued making waves. Perhaps a little over-zealously he began to haul in his nets, but he was impatient to see the size of the catch. The first rippling glimmer of black and silver bodies, trapped and wriggling, encouraged him to intensify his efforts. The more enmeshed they became, the more frantically they flashed and struggled in the ever more crowded, ever smaller spaces, until one mighty sweep dropped them into his hold and there they lay, flapping and gasping, finally to be persuaded that they had been not so much caught, as saved.

The wash from this hectic evangelical trawling rocked the Maximum Angel, President of all the Chapters, out of his catalepsy. It was many years since this supreme lord had clawed and hacked his way to the power he maintained by means of the simple but successful strategy of total bloody retaliation for any offence, real or imagined. "All on one and one on all!" had been his war cry, and he bore the scars of many battles in which his single fury had routed multiple opponents. The gaps in his mouth, however, were not war wounds. To bind his followers to him, to seal their loyalty, he extracted his own teeth with a pair of pliers in exchange for beer at a public house run by a biker. "An eye for an eye and a tooth for a pint!" was the maxim by which he consolidated his rule. But lately, aware of the setting of his sun and the rising Angels lurking in the wings, he had become obsessive about knives assembling to plunge into his iron-studded back. And here was another snipe at his authority. He tugged at the horns of his helmet and scratched his hairy belly where it bulged beneath his waistcoat. He had blown all his options long ago. Altering his position was a luxury he could not afford. Yet he could not deal with the matter personally either. It would leave his power base too vulnerable. He looked around at his entourage, but their bristling reflexes would only endow the clergyman with a kind of martyrdom. "He'th got to be thtopped thomehow," he muttered, wondering how to achieve this and at the same time not appear to be taking the threat seriously.

"Who has?" asked an attendant mamma with the looks of a lobotomised Botticelli goddess. She mashed his food and emptied a can of bitter into his metal tankard.

"Fffreewheeling Fffrank." The Maximum Angel slurped his meal and recalled Reverend Adams' passion for the girls. A plan congealed and with a satisfied belch he said to her, "I'll thend YOU. Or better thtill, I'll GIVE him to you. Do what you like with him. He'th yourth."

Smiling like a delinquent Delilah she installed herself on the back of Reverend Adams' motorcycle and gripped him with carmine talons and fishnet thighs. She was all that he had dreamed of, and more, for being real. He nibbled at the bait until, with a practised manoeuvre she forced him to swallow hook, line and sinker. Like a multitude of Samsons before him, he floundered, enraptured, on a treacherous lee shore. The Parochial Church Council had waited for such a moment and quickly seized the initiative. Reverend Adams was made to resign. The Angels were banished. A few diplomatic extractions had unwittingly helped to pave the way.

"Things have gone a bit pear-shaped," he explained to his spiritual consultant.

The superior blinked. "From where I'm sitting it looks like a complete fiasco. What happened to the old killer instinct?"

Reverend Adams wondered how best to reply. "Perhaps we can keep things simmering on the back burner and review the situation when the dust has settled."

"The competition will be in there like a bullet. You might as well just hand it to him on a plate." He frowned and fidgetted with his watch but his gaze ebbed and flowed over the Botticelli mamma as she fingered the joystick on his personal computer, her chthonic charms bathed by the monitor's leafy glow.

Beneath the arcadian tresses clicked a brain with megabyte capacity. While the clergymen lobbed recriminations she studied the software manuals. To the Hell's Angels, hi-tech meant the latest motorcycle refinement. Computers were what you played saloon bar war games on. But as she turned over the pages, bright new vistas unfolded, ripe with promise, there for the taking. She gingerly experimented with a few lines of BASIC and was surprised by the warm electronic response. Her fingers tapped as her mind delved into programming techniques, spinning sparkling chains of logic. The keyboard hummed and the VDU danced to her tunes. Defenceless against this microfascination, faint in its user friendly embrace, ravished by hardware expansion potential, she was utterly seduced. "Here is Knowledge," temptation hissed behind her ear, "Here is Power. With compatible graphics and a few hundred K of RAM, you can access the Infinite." She had to have it all.

Like a basilisk the Botticelli mamma locked eyes with the spiritual consultant and saw purple irises glitter behind his tinted lenses. Slowly she unzipped her star-studded jacket and, between constellations, produced a plump, perfect peach. "Hungry?" she asked, offering it. The superior's eyes moved from her Elysian asymmetry to the red and gold orb she held out towards him. As he looked, everything in the room, in the universe, receded until there was only the succulent fruit, pungent, pervasive, irresistible.

Soon the media were flashing and buzzing like an amusement arcade. The Maximum Angel's illustrated chequebook memoirs gave an astronomical boost to gutter tabloid circulation figures. On consecutive Sunday mornings the spiritual consultant perused this apocrypha and wondered how to bring about a comparable upturn in his own fortunes. Adjusting his spectacles he looked from Reverend Adams to the girl and back again. It would be easy to play the competition at its own game, he reflected. After all, they shared some very marketable commodities. But to have any real chance of seeing him off required an aggressive, pro-active new strategy. At the very least the customers would sit up and take notice. However, with careful imagineering and a good following wind his back burners could blaze into unprecedented pillars of flame. The competition would be dimmed into insignificance. All the credit would be his.

"We're retargetting our mission," he said briskly, "And we'll need to give it our very best shot."

Reverend Adams is now a celebrity. He showers daily and has his stubble professionally trimmed. Over his clerical collar he wears hand-tailored designer-label clothing, sometimes made of leather. Membership of the All Angels Church of the Air is soaring. "It is better to sin and be forgiven than never to sin at all!" he cries, straight into the camera's eye. The studio lights glare hotly. His message rings through the lounges of the nation. Television audiences from all walks of life pause to hear him and post their enthusiastic witness as directed. In lecture halls, conference centres and sports stadia he markets a Redemption Policy which offers alluring bonuses in addition to a guaranteed yield. This is the brainchild of the Botticelli mamma whose born-again smile endorses every promise. The spiritual consultant fiddles with his watch as actual and projected returns twinkle on the computer screen. "They're licking the crumbs from his hands," he sighs with satisfaction.

"Say YES to Life!" Reverend Adams' cry is fervent amid the strobing special effects. Cameras pan and zoom as the gospel group and rock band explode with the refrain, "Yeah to Life!" The assembly joins in, arms raised, hands linked, "Yeah to Life!" It is a hit. The applause is seismic. He is a star. But during rare meditative moments, or when the clamour of cosmic motorcycles drives away sleep, he ponders on the implications of having your cake and eating it.

Thomas E. Kennedy
A BERLIN OF THE MIND

"And there followed another angel, saying,
Babylon is fallen, fallen, that great city,
because she made all nations drink of the
wine of the wrath of her fornication."
Revelations 14:8

"We turn on the spit of our desire."
Milo Mendoza, *American Nights*

From the window of a tower that rose behind the other side of the
wall, a young East German soldier watched Turner through
binoculars. Turner stood on the iron platform, staring back over
the wall's rolling lip, across the desolate zone of emptiness to the
tower window. He could see the German's clean, scrubbed cheek,
his blond hair, the rough grey wool of his uniform. He could see
the young man's lips, pictured him going off duty in the evening,
home to kiss the mouths of wife and children in a simple
apartment in the clean city.

The soldier lowered his binoculars. His eyes were blue. The
sky behind the tower was blue. Turner felt an attraction to the
young man which was almost carnal. He nodded. The soldier
made no sign. Turner nodded again. He understood the young
man's hesitation. He climbed down the platform's metal steps to
Pottsdamplatz. The wall furled out in either direction like a ribbon
of concrete, scribbled and stained with graffiti - a solid mass of
clashing, overlapping, underlapping colour, wayward strokes,
scrawls, scribbles upon scribbles, a mix so interdigested as to

13

become even drabber and more depressing than bare grey concrete. It seemed such a mindless disrespect for this functioning symbol of division that Turner felt ashamed of freedom, of the idle, foolish use to which it was put on this side of a wall designed to enforce its denial.

He started moving again through the late afternoon sunlight, following the wall, surveying the splash of images that unrolled along it: a broken skull beneath the caption *Big Skull Science*; elaborately block-lettered mottoes: *Our dream is your disaster - Dead Kennedys*; a bizarre-winged creature paring its toenails in a horseshoe-wreathed caption, *The sleep of reason produces monsters*. Side by side at one stretch on the rim of the Kreutzberg were a pair of contrasting images: a huge grey face peering hungrily from behind a grey chain-link fence with one link severed; the zipper of an enormous fly tugged halfway down to reveal the green idyll of a garden where the pubis would be.

Turner paused to study the last one, the unzipped garden. It then occurred to him that the zipper was not meant to be on trousers, but on the wall itself.

Behind him, a voice whispered, "Hey, you, *Deutscher*: You fick mit Trallala."

Turner glanced, saw a dark man, a Turk perhaps, with full lips, black coily hair. Turner ignored him, kept moving, but the man circled round to cut him off.

"Hey. *Deutscher*."

Turner said, "I'm not German. And I'm not interested, thank you."

The lid of the man's right eye sagged beneath the weight of a shiny red growth. "*Deutscher, Deutscher*: big kicks, *nicht*? Big Sexyland. Nonstop kino. Club You unt Me. Zpezial wishes, look!" The Turk drew a photograph from inside his jacket. Turner looked at it: a toad-eyed dwarf with an enormous erect phallus sat astride a corpulent, black-haired woman whose mouth was bridled. The woman's eyes stared out above the leather and metal between her teeth; they looked like some other creature trapped inside her skull; their gaze entered Turner's mind.

The Turk grinned.

Turner said, "Put your damned pictures away. I don't *want* them. I don't want them in my mind."

The Turk giggled and palmed the photograph into his breast pocket. His fingernails were long and polished, though rimmed beneath with dirt. Turner began to move more quickly. He sensed the Turk hanging behind him, closed his eyes to block out the image from the photograph, the woman's eyes, Eileen's eyes, his little daughter, the children who had to grow up in this filthy world.

As he moved in away from the wall towards Kreutzberg, he watched the road for a taxi. He passed a cinder block apartment house, a red-brick church with twin towers, its dome topped with green copper angels, stepped over a single, rotted shoe, abandoned in the muddy gutter, stiletto heel cracked, heard or thought he heard the Turk's nasal whisper, "Hey, *Deutscher*, you fick mit Trallala. Sexy, oh! Big meat, *nicht?*"

A taxi cruised past, but did not stop at his wave. Turkish music drifted from an open doorway. He passed a shop window heaped with smashed-in television sets. A naked-armed man with green hair and nose jewelry leaned against the door jamb, watching him pass. Turner's heart felt like meat.

A silver Mercedes taxi idled at the corner. Turner lunged for it. "The Grunewald, please. Brahmstrasse."

He watched the Turk grinning from a street door after him as the can made a U-turn and reeled away. Turner leaned back against the fabric-covered seats, blotted his forehead with a square of handkerchief, saw the driver's eyes watching him in the rear-view mirror, shifted, saw his own face there: self-portrait of excess: map of drink down his scholar's nose, bleached eyes weary of desire.

"You like Berlin?" the driver asked.

"I'm resting. I'm here to rest."

The driver smiled into the mirror. "You don't got to rest here until you an old man."

Turner shook his head, closed his mouth, watched the cab glide past the Metropole, saw above the entrance a frieze of lovers or naked wrestlers, he couldn't tell which. His intention had been

15

to stay clear of the city's belly. He wished to avoid the distractions of the Ku'damm, the flesh-houses and drag shows, the sex shops and whipping rooms and slender young German women with their soulful eyes and skin-tight leotards.

He was here for the wall. He was here to see where east and west lay nose to nose, to know this place of jumping over, to be within its reach and look across to the Other.

As the cab turned into Brahmstrasse, his nerves calmed. He lowered his eyelids and heard lullabies as they glided beneath the sheltering trees of the Grunewald to the Schlosshotel.

He took his evening meal in the hotel restaurant, sat afterwards sipping the last of his sec and gazing at the carved wood sylvan figures banded along the moulding of the high ceiling as the light outside faded hue by hue to darkness. He felt safe, decided to order more wine, looked up and saw an elderly gentleman approaching. He nodded politely. Turner returned the greeting, and the man stopped before him. "May I choin you, sir?"

"Of course. Please." Turner motioned to the chair across the table, but the man sat beside him. His hair was grey and wild, the shoulders and lapel of his dark jacket flaked with dandruff and scraps of hair. Turner wished to dust the jacket off. He looked away.

"*Englisch?*" the old German asked.

Turner shook his head. The man was so close that his dark cuff was brushing the melting pat of butter on Turner's bread dish. "American."

"Indeed." Light glinted off the old man's spectacles, obscuring his eyes. "Und are you enchoying Berlin?"

"I'm here to rest really. To get away."

"Ah? From what, *cher ami*?"

Turner's fingers trembled as he lit a cigarette. He no longer wished to speak, but could in his anxiety see no way out. "I've not been well, my nerves, you see. My wife... Berlin, it seems so clear and pure."

The German stared at him.

Turner thought of Eileen, the parties, the drink, thought of the children, so young still. He thought of the Star Wars figures they had requested when he asked what he should bring back for them. He had stood in the toy shop at the airport, studying them. Some of the monsters, he knew, were symbols of good, but he didn't know which and couldn't determine it by their appearance. So he bought them all; then, outside the shop, he came face to face with the realisation of what he was contemplating, that he might never see their young faces again, and he dropped the bag of toy figures into a refuse can and fled from it.

The old German was still watching him. His spectacles had slipped down on the bridge of his nose, revealing a red growth on his trembling eyelid. Turner stared. The man was smiling. Abruptly, the Turk's photograph reappeared in Turner's mind.

"This is a *filthy* city," he snapped and rose, flinging his soiled napkin to the table.

The old German raised his brow.

"Forgive me," Turner said quickly. "I'm not well." His heels reported sharply across the marble floor.

He smoked a cigarette in the garden. Stood in the agreeable September chill watching the night green trees and misted sky, trying to see his place in the truest order of things. The hotel at his back was a nest of turn-of-the-century copies of the antiquities commissioned by a steel merchant. It was all fake - fake Rembrandts in ornate frames, fake Roman murals, fake Sistine ceilings, a fake castle. He recalled again watching Eileen with two men while the children slept upstairs. He breathed, thought, exhaled, saw his dead breath catch light from the moon.

In his room, he sat in an armchair and glanced idly through a folder of literature the management had provided on the desktop. The brochure announced a downtown "MacDonald's Cup" bicycle race, sponsored by the local MacDonald Hamburger emporium. Another, which purported to be a map of the city, was fringed round with ads featuring photos or sketches of half-naked women: *Intim, pikant, exotisch, erotischste, Lady Lydia Domina aus Passion, phantasievoll, Club Petite Surprise, Lady Bizarr...* Turner flung the map into the waste pail and paced the room, muttering curses.

He ended at the bathroom mirror, watching himself place pills on his filmed tongue, drink water, stare into his wasted face until his eyes began to droop.

He woke smiling to the sound of chill air fingering the brittle leaves outside his window. He rose briskly, did push-ups on the carpet before the open window, breakfasted on cold meats and cheese, brushed his teeth, voided, showered, shaved, patted his jowls with stinging fluids. He tied a paisley scarf beneath the collar of his blue serge shirt and set off on foot for the wall, strong again, determined.

On one shoulder he carried a pair of binoculars in a black leather case. In his breast pocket was his passport and all of his money and credit cards, which he intended to dispose of at the earliest possible moment, a small spiral pad and his silver cross pen. He had left the photographs of Eileen and the children on the desk in his room. Leaving them there had taken resolution, a moment of decision torn from his heart, a victory over love. The sensation had been not unlike the experience of deciding to remove an old bandage crusted upon a healing wound: You look at it, know it will hurt, bleed; you fear, decide, tear. And then it's over.

The morning sun lit gold on the wings and robe of the Victoria Angel on its pedestal above the city's scummy streets. Turner could not determine from his map whether the angel were on this side or the other. He headed toward its gleaming wings, but in the looping of a side-street lost it, found himself again at the wall, climbed up the metal steps to the observation platform. He put his binoculars to his eyes, saw the young East German soldier watching him from the tower opposite.

Turner trained his binoculars to right and left of the tower. He could not see beyond the seventy-five metre zone of desolation. Midway across, a Doberman paused, one paw raised in mid-motion, glared. Turner's field of vision encompassed barbed wire, wilted grass, deserted pathways, park lamps, strobes, the wall here, the wall there, the tower, the young German watching him.

He returned his glasses to their leather case and climbed down again. At the base of the wall, three young men in metal-studded leather slacks stood drinking bottles of brown water sugared with caramel. Their teeth were edged in brown, and they were sharing a cellophane bag of crisped fat clumps. Their fingers and lips and cheeks glistened with the grease. Stencilled on the wall behind them was a multi-coloured series of the Statue of Liberty in black, white, pink, lavender, green. The three young men watched Turner. One raised the middle finger of his left hand and flicked it upwards, dark eyes smouldering beneath dark brows, begging Turner for an excuse.

Emotion staked Turner's heart: hatred, desire, fear, disgust. Rage simmered in him. He wanted to fight them. Let them kill me, *filth!* He slung the binocular case off his shoulder, stopped, glared at them. He wanted to fling the case at them. Smash one of their brazen faces. Their feet shifted. They looked away. Turner felt power, tested it by remaining another moment. They would not meet his gaze. He felt the light of fierceness filling his eyes as he headed away from them back into the city, the light of righteousness, wrath.

At the mouth of the *U-Bahn*, the Turk waited, grinning. His teeth were scored with a yellow stripe of childhood rickets. Turner focused the light of his eyes upon him. *Please*, he thought. *Try something. Anything.* But the Turk only grinned as Turner passed, descended the stair to the subway.

On the platform, two men argued over a bottle of gin. Their shirts stretched at the buttons over their guts, and their knuckles were scabbed and cut. A tall slender young man with pink hair was kissing a woman with patches of acne at the pit of each cheek. A child with dull black eyes chewed a bar of chocolate. Posters on the walls advertised cigarettes, whiskey, candy, condoms. A fat woman with dirty hands sat on a bench and read a book whose cover depicted a doctor and nurse kissing.

The train rolled into the station. Turner opened the door and boarded, sat beside a middle-aged woman clutching a cardboard suitcase. A woman seated across from him made him think of Eileen - her eyes, perhaps, so pale, her slender fingers. He steeled himself to tear off another bandage. *Goodbye,* he thought. *Goodbye.* A word so strange, demanding, frightful; a word that drew boundaries upon his will: you can do this; she will be left; they will be away from you; you will join the other.

He leaned his head back on the window glass behind him and thought: *Commie. Jew. Russian. Kraut. Cunt.*

The Friederichstrasse station made his stomach move. Not a single poster or notice marred the uniform green drabness of the walls. His breath was shallow. To stand in a roomful of people in a public station devoid of advertisements had an eerie feel to it. There is no business here. No business. He was afraid. He saw again Eileen with the two men and the babies asleep upstairs and his business office, the receptions, drinks, sugar-rotted teeth of that world of yesterday, please God... But God, he knew, had died to make way for greater themes.

A muscular young man with sensuous lips and blond moustache, a diamond in his ear-lobe and shirt open to the sternum, stared at Turner. An East German policeman emerged from a booth, shook his head, handed papers back to the young man, escorted him back to the subway. Another policeman came out, steering a girl away, motioning impatiently for her to button her blouse up to her throat. The girl's hair was electric blue, and she wore a pin through the centre of her nose.

Turner prayed. *Please, God, let me come over.* As his line dwindled toward the invisible screening place, he watched people disappear through to the other side: a middle-aged man wearing a fat tie and carrying cardboard boxes with twine handles; a woman in an autumn coat and fur collars; a mother and child; a black man; a couple.

When Turner entered the inspection tunnel, he saw chill blue eyes inspecting him, his passport, him, his passport.

"*Funf Mark,*" a mouth said.

Turner paid, was motioned through, paid again, received a crisp piece of east currency, climbed stairs through unpostered walls up to the street.

On this side, the sun shone. A parade was in progress. Smiling workers with good strong teeth carried red banners that flowed in an even-currented wind. Men and women, clean people in modest, clean clothing, of equal height, all walking in pace.

Turner backed against a wall, dazzled, questioning what he saw, challenging it to be certain it were real before he would accept it.

The parade was swift. Glockenspiels, drums, brass, smiles of strong good teeth. A blushing woman glanced at him from the ranks. Their eyes met. She looked so glad, right into his eyes, and Turner looked back at her as at a sister, fellow human, all of them, fellows of this world, brothers, sisters. The rattling chimes of the glockenspiels rolled past, trailing away with the tail end of the parade.

Turner strolled: along the bank of the River Spree, past the Pergamon. He strolled the length of Unter Den Linten, beneath the small yellow leaves of September, to the Brandenburg Gate, staring west now across the zone of desolation to the dirty city of the west.

He turned his back on it, gazed down the broad quiet boulevard of Lindens, free of the stinking belch of traffic. He recalled pictures from the forties of Hitler on the balcony as military parades rolled past his crooked salute, and the nostalgic grandeur of the image consisted in the fact of the annihilation of its source - cleared away for a new history to begin a new course. He strolled back toward the centre with an easy sense of conquered destiny as the afternoon shadows began to lengthen, followed to Alexanderplatz, a peaceful vast expanse of open square surrounded at comfortable spacings by buildings, some new, some old. The ancient Marienkirche stood with its red-brown steeple before the looming modern Teletower and the pastel skyscrapers with reflector windows. The church's grandeur was humble beside its tall, young neighbours.

Turner gazed up at the Teletower. *L'heure bleu* was approaching. He entered the tower and joined the queue waiting to ride an elevator to the top of the city.

He sat at a table 207 metres up in a café that slowly revolved within the tower's globe. He drank *Berliner kidl* and *doppelkorn schnapps*, iced to a mist, and watched the city turn below him. He could see the island of the west nestled in the shell of its wall, connected by a fenced-off highway through East Germany to the other end of Europe. Alongside the winding River Spree below, a white-topped train snaked through the East. Inside the tower the light was low, darkening gradually with the blueness of the city. The *doppelkorn* chilled his lips to an agreeable numbness.

At the table across from him, a young German family sat eating ice cream. The mother glanced at Turner with large brown eyes. Her child's blond head lay in her lap; she and her husband's hands were touching on the tablecloth, but her eye's held Turner's. Her lips were full, chiselled, and her dark hair fell in curls across her forehead. Turner drew his gaze free, stared out of the window again and saw the last fading of the light. Pale copper street lamps flanked the roads. Here and there the headlights of automobiles cast wandering beams. And a sadness that showed itself only in the dark seeped toward him.

The brown eyes still watched him. Turner looked at her hair, the graceful line of her shoulders. Her breasts were full; the nipples pressed against her blouse. She turned away. Light glistened on the surface of an open sore at the corner of her mouth. And from behind Turner a voice whispered, "*Deutscher*, hey. You fick mit Trallala. Big meat. What you like, *nicht?*"

Turner froze. His mouth opened. Then he was rising. "Enough," he hissed. Louder: "*Enough.*" Bellowing, "*E-nough!*" - as he rose, turned, saw the hated face, swung his fist at the sagging eyelid, missed, swung again, felt knuckle bone bite soft lip. The Turk fell backward off his chair, blood smeared around his mouth. He scrabbled away on hands and knees, but Turner's fingers clutched into the oily hair and jerked. The Turk cried out. Turner was upon him, thumbs searching the stringy neck to find the windpipe. The Turk gagged. Spit flecked the corner of his mouth. Turner's thumbs pressed, squeezed. He glared into the eyes, the sagging eyelid, and his thumbs dug deeper into soft throat, felt the passion of destruction. He did not realise that he was grinning until he saw the pained glee reflected in the eyes of the dying Turk.

Turner jerked his hands away. The Turk coughed, gulped in air, eyes all the while lit with pleasure as they stared into Turner's.

Then hands were seizing Turner from behind, dragging him away. The Turk watched, sitting up on the floor, his sagging eyelid, his lip curled in amusement.

The duty officer was the man Turner had watched through his binoculars: young, blond, clean-faced. On his right hand he wore a wedding band. His eyes, gazing upon Turner, were chill, his mouth without sympathy.

"Vi haf your name, Mister Turner," he said. "Vi haf your name on paper. Vi do not wish you to return here no more. You are not welcome. Now you must go out of zis land unt return to the vest, Mister Turner. Forefer."

Turner said, "I watched you. From the other side. I loved you, your life. Do you have a family? Children?"

The German officer glanced at the sergeant who waited by the door. "This vill be all," he said. The sergeant stepped forward. The young officer spoke in German to him; then, without looking at Turner, he left the room.

Turner said, "I came in good faith. I came with love in my heart for this land."

"*Ja, ja,*" said the sergeant calmly and took hold of Turner's bicep as though it were the handle of a suitcase. He smelt of sensen and chilly grey wool.

"You are all in danger, sergeant," Turner said. "Corruption and decay are just around the corner."

"*Ja, ja,*" said the sergeant, lifting Turner to his feet.

"You go bye-bye now."

Slowly, Turner climbed up out of the *U-Bahn* onto the Ku'damm, to the rev and beep and stench of traffic, the quick jerky movement along the boulevard. From a shop front, electric boogie rhythms bumped ceaselessly. A magazine rack at the mouth of the station displayed a long row of naked body parts: lips, breasts, buttocks, thighs rising into the shadows of intimate clothing.

Turner's eyes swept along the rack semi-consciously, came to the end. The Turk slouched there against the wall, grinning, his shirt collar pulled open to reveal the bruises, his full red lip distended, dried blood between his teeth. Turner's eyes continued in their sweep past him, though not without having seen the shiny red growth that weighed down the sagging right eyelid.

"Hey, *Deutscher*," the Turk whispered, and nothing more. His swollen lips smiled. His eyes presumed intimacy. "You *Deutscher*," he whispered, as to a lover.

Turner said nothing. He kept walking, pretending that he had seen nothing, heard nothing, felt nothing, desired nothing.

James Lansbury
A SMALL BETRAYAL

I eased the top off my bottle of beer. Mandy turned her steak.

"I'm used to warm Pennine beer," I said, laughing.

"Then you'd better be careful," Mandy replied. "This beer goes straight to your head. Especially when it's ice-cold."

"Four of these and I'm anybody's," I said, and I laughed nervously, and certainly much louder than was necessary. It was only my second bottle and already I was feeling the effects.

Mandy didn't seem to notice. She was pre-occupied with getting her steaks just right.

"Melvyn's accent was as strong as yours when he first arrived out here," Mandy said, without even looking up from the pieces of meat and chicken. "In fact, you remind me of him quite a lot."

Now she looked up at me, as if searching for further points of similarity. I noticed her attractive blonde hair and bare freckled shoulders.

I had spoken to Melvyn earlier in the evening, and at work too. There had been no trace of any accent at all, even though it was true that we both hailed from the same northern town. Despite the similarity in our origins, I had quickly concluded that I had nothing to say to him. It was quite clear to me that Melvyn had deliberately modified his accent, and in those days that, to me, smacked of... well, a sort of betrayal, I suppose.

All this happened a long time ago, when I was young and green, and in those days I thought that how a person talked mattered. The young man I was then, and the person I am now - to be truthful, we have very little in common except a name and some memories.

I had been in Malambia for only a few weeks. While I didn't actually wander round the streets with my mouth open - I was never that naive - I readily admit I was very rough at the edges, yet prepared to be surprised and even astonished by Africa.

This was my very first time away from home. Yes, I had once spent a week in Paris, and another in London, but I had never actually left home. So my parents were very surprised to learn that I had applied for a post with a mining company in Malambia, and so soon after gaining my qualification as a teacher. To start with, my parents did not even know where Malambia was. Few people did; the country had recently changed its name on becoming independent. My mother became tearful, believing all Africa to be jungle, warriors and wild animals. My father said very little, except to warn me to take care, and always remember where I came from. For my father, remembering one's origins was always a mark of integrity.

The interview was in London. There were three people to ask me questions. One was Dave Turner, who had travelled to London especially to interview candidates on behalf of the Ministry of Mines. Before the individual interviews, there were group discussions. This was a weeding-out process. I must have said the right things, because not only was I asked to proceed to the individual interview in the afternoon, but Dave Turner assured me I would get his vote.

I had not been in Malambia very long when the invitations started to arrive. Dinner parties for six people or eight perhaps, at which there was always an unattached girl, all peaches and cream. The winks and nudges were anything but subtle, and it was difficult to decide who was the more embarrassed, me or the girl.

Then there were the barbecues. We called them 'braais', which was short for the Afrikaner word 'braaivleis', meaning 'meat-burning'. I remember how the smoke from the braai seemed to pursue me, no matter where I stood. People laughed at my efforts to avoid the smoke. It was the same with mosquitoes. Unerringly, they came for my white, tender skin, as yet untouched by the glare of the sun. I suspect that people laughed at my gaucheness too, but I did not mind too much, believing it was better to be a source of laughter than to be ignored.

The very first braai that I attended was at Dave's house. He had a fine bungalow, with a large swimming pool, pellucidly clean. The invitation did not come directly from Dave Turner himself; our paths had not yet crossed at work. A mining colleague had told me that such evenings were open to anybody. It did not matter who turned up at Dave's, so long as they brought a bottle. I purchased a cheap, pleasant Paarl wine, which you could still buy in Malambia in those days.

Partly because I was shy, and partly because I felt to be a gatecrasher, and because I did not know the ropes, I was rather late in getting my pieces of steak and going to the braai. In fact I had to be dragged there by Mandy Turner. She had found me in a quiet corner, trying not to be conspicuous, waiting for the moment when I could slip quietly away.

So, by the time I reached the braai, everyone else had finished cooking. The charcoal was a low hot glow. There were only the two of us. Mandy must have been all of forty years old, but she had kept her slim figure. Her tan put my pinkness to shame.

She poured beer all over the steaks.

"Dave likes his well done and yet tender," Mandy said.

"Keeps them succulent, does it, the beer?" I asked.

"As far as Dave's concerned, it's the beer that matters, not the steak," she said.

I could just see Dave Turner, standing on the long front verandah, sleeves rolled up to reveal thick hairy forearms. He had a can of beer in his hand. So did his friends. I had already noticed that the consumption of alcohol among my expatriate colleagues was alarmingly high: much higher than I was accustomed to seeing back... back home.

"So," Mandy said, "now that you've been here a while, what do you think of them?"

She had just speared a sausage and was holding it up for inspection.

"I like them," I said.

"Do you?" Her voice hardly changed in pitch and tone, and

yet her two questioning words conveyed both surprise and contempt.

"They're a lot spicier than I expected," I added.

Mandy laughed. It was a brittle laugh, very clear.

"No, I didn't mean the sausages, luv. I meant... them."

She was close to me now, and her perfume was strong in the hot October evening.

What I wanted to say, and ought to have said, was that it was their country now, for good or ill, and in any case they were individuals and human beings just like us, and the old colonial days were finished, but, instead, I made a fatuous remark about sausages. When I noticed that she was not laughing, I said, "I'm sorry, Mrs Turner."

"Mandy. Please. Call me Mandy," she replied.

Her perfume, which ought to have crept up on me insidiously, was like a frontal assault.

"I was being formal," I said, "because - well, you are the wife of the chief metal salesman."

"Look, luv," Mandy said, "out here class barriers aren't as rigid as in the UK. Sure, you're only a teacher... "

I was not offended. My job description said I was an Education and Training Officer, but I knew the value of such titles.

"...but that doesn't matter out here."

She laughed and threw back her head. The skin on her throat was not as youthful as her laugh.

As the only black person in the house that evening was a servant giving out drinks, there was no need for me to ask what criterion really mattered. In any case, I told myself, it was foolish to fall out with people unnecessarily. In fact, I had already been warned, at a dinner party earlier in the week, that it would be wise to maintain good relations with colleagues. After all, within two years I might be seeking another tour of duty, and if I wanted to obtain another contract with the mining company... well, old chap, if you haven't kept your nose clean, eh? I was quickly learning that one was more prized for social skills than for academic qualifications.

"Be a darling and get me another beer," Mandy smiled.

I guessed the beer would be for Dave's steak, so I asked her what she was drinking.

"Gin and tonic, luv," she said.

"And I'll have a beer," I added. "It'll be my third."

"And four and you're anybody's," Mandy quoted my own words back at me.

I blushed. She smiled.

The barman, a round man with a shining black face, gave me two beers. Then I asked for the gin and tonic. He asked if I wanted ice in the gin. I told him I would check.

"Is it for the donna?" he asked.

"Pardon?"

"The Madam. Mrs Turner."

"Yes, yes. For the... the donna."

He put ice in the glass.

"Mrs Turner. She always take plenty ice, bwana."

I thought that he looked rather hard at me as he spoke. Yet I thanked him and returned to the braai.

"Oh bless you, luv."

Mandy's voice tinkled, like ice against the side of the glass.

She poured yet more beer liberally over the steaks.

"There's only two things they're interested in," Mandy said. "Booze and rugby. Other things... "

"Yes?" I prompted quietly.

"Well, there are other things, but they can only think of them."

"The hot climate?"

"The booze, luv. The demon drink. It doesn't lend itself to... "
She allowed her voice to trail away.

"There's something about it in *Macbeth*," I told her. "The Porter's scene."

"Oh!" Her eyes were suddenly bright. "Are you interested in theatre?"

"I once played in a Priestley comedy," I told her.

"What did you play? A Bradford millionaire?"

Mandy burst out laughing. I put it down to the warmth of the evening and the effects of the gin.

29

"Only a small part," I said.

"Oh," she pouted, "I wouldn't have thought you was a man for a small part."

Her voice had dropped to a whisper. She traced the outside of her glass with her forefinger.

"With more experience, I might tackle larger roles," I replied.

I stared straight into her eyes; she didn't look away. Then she sipped her gin and tonic, while I gulped down half my beer.

"You've got a very nice house," I said. "Nicely furnished, I mean."

"We can afford it," Mandy said.

"How does one get to be a chief metal salesman?" I asked.

In all my life I had never before used the word 'one' in this way. Although separated from my parents by seven thousand miles, I felt a stab of guilt.

"What do you mean, luv?"

Her bare shoulder was cool against my arm.

"I mean, which university did Mr Turner attend?"

"University? Dave? You must be joking!"

"But - "

"He started work on this mine as a fitter."

"Then he's done very well for himself," I said, prepared to admire ability.

"A lot of people cleared off at Independence. Dave stayed on. He happened to be in the right place at the right time."

"It can't be as simple as that, surely?"

"And he gets on well with people. That's important."

My steak and sausages were now ready. I filled my plate with roast potatoes and salad.

"We can eat out here," Mandy said. "Much cooler than the house."

Two chairs and a table were already set in place beside a bougainvillea.

"Beautiful plants," I said.

"The bougainvillea? Oh, yes. The flowers last most of the year."

I had recently been doing a lot of reading and one of the

things I had learned was what appear to be flowers on the bougainvillea are really modified leaves. The actual flower is so poor a thing that no insect would ever be attracted to it. But I said nothing; after all, there was no point in upsetting someone over so trivial a point, and this was her house, after all.

After we had eaten, Mandy suggested that we go indoors and dance. One of the rooms had been cleared. There was a copper clock on the wall and a couple of Tretchikoff reproductions. In those days I was not a proficient dancer. Mandy Turner had to guide me. She noticed me gazing at the dark faces of the Malay women in the reproductions.

"Nice, aren't they?" she said.

"Yes, very nice," I agreed.

"Would you like to look all round the house?"

From the verandah came the guffaws of men who have just heard the punch line of a broad joke.

"Get me a gin and tonic, luv."

I went to the bar to ask for Mandy's drink and my beer. The black servant gave me a long stare, almost a look of insolence, I thought.

I eased the top off my nottle of beer, took a long drink, and followed Mandy along a corridor.

FEN FARM

WRITING COURSES

Five-day Residential courses at Fen Farm. Top quality Tutor/Writers usually arrive late Monday afternoon and leave on Friday morning. Those attending a course are expected to arrive Monday and leave on Saturday morning around 10.00 a.m.

Fen Farm stands in seven acres of farmland opposite a wooded fen in the small unspoiled village of Blo Norton in the heart of East Anglia, between Diss and Thetford. The 17c thatched farm-house is heavily beamed with log burning inglenook fireplaces. Informal readings and discussions take place in the farmhouse.

The comfortable converted barn is where visitors will sleep, eat and work. Bedrooms are carpeted and comfortable, but members should expect to share. There is also a spacious heated studio with desks and type-writers.

There is no entrance qualification for a five-day course, the only requirements are, a strong desire to write, typing paper, a note-pad and something to write with. People of all ages over sixteen are welcome , whether they are writing seriously for the first time or have had work published.

Courses provide the opportunity for eight people to work with an established writer in a relaxed setting. Tutors will not give formal teaching, but are there to share their skills and give personal advice during Tuesdays, Wednesdays and Thursdays.

The fee for a course, all food, tuition and accommodation is £195. This does not represent the true cost of a place as the fee is kept relatively low because of funding from the Eastern Arts Board. Some grants will be available for students and others in the region who would otherwise be unable to join us because the fee is beyond their means.

Anyone arriving by train can be met at Diss or Thetford Station, if you let us know in advance. For those travelling by car, a map and directions will be supplied. There is ample parking space at Fen Farm.

Supported by the **Eastern Arts** Board

Contact: Sally Worboyes, 10 Angel Hill, Bury St. Edmunds, Suffolk IP33 1UZ.
Telephone: 0284 753110 or 0379 898741

Herta Müller

ROTTEN PEARS

Translated by Agnes Stein

The gardens are a stinging green. Fences swim towards their wet shadows. Window panes slide naked, shining from one house to the next. The steeple turns, the memorial cross turns. The heroes' names are many and blurred. Kathe reads the names from bottom to top. The third from the bottom is my grandfather, she says. She swipes at the cross in front of the church. In front of the mill a pond glitters. The duckweeds are green eyes. A fat snake lives in the reeds, Kathe says. The night watchman has seen it. By day it eats ducks and fish. At night it creeps to the mill and eats bran and flour. The left-over flour is wet with its spit. The miller empties it into the pond because it is poisonous.

The fields are lying on their belly. Up above in the clouds they stand on their heads. The roots of the sunflowers tie up the clouds. Father's hands turn the steering wheel. In the small window behind the tomato crate I see Father's hair. The auto speeds. The village sinks into the blue. I can no longer see the church steeple. I see my aunt's thighs close to my father's trouser legs.

Houses pass by along the pavement. The houses are not a village because I don't live here. Small men with puffed-up trouser legs pass like strangers through the streets. On narrow rattling bridges the skirts of foreign women flutter. Children with lean naked thighs stand about singly without pants under a number of tall trees. Their hands hold an apple. They do not eat. They wave. They call with empty mouths. Kathe waves briefly and does not look back. I wave for some time. I look at their skinny thighs until they dissolve and I see only tall trees.

The plain lies below the hill. In our village the sky holds the hills. They won't fall through the clouds into the plain. We've already gone far, Kathe says and yawns into the sun. Father throws a glowing cigarette out of the window. Our aunt moves her hand as she talks.

The plums between the fences are small and green. Cows stand in the grass and chew as they gaze at the dust of the wheels. The ground climbs out of the grass over bare stones, over roots and bark. Kathe says: those are mountains and the stones are cliffs.

Shrubs at the side of the wheels wave to the aeroplane. Water rushes from their roots. The fern drinks and shakes its lacy web. The car rides on narrow grey paths. These are called serpentines, Kathe says. The paths become crumpled. I say, our village lies deep down in the hills. Kathe laughs: the hills are here in the mountains and our village is in the plain, she says.

White kilometer stones stare at me. Half of Father's face rises over the steering wheel. Our aunt grabs Father's ear.

Tiny birds hop from branch to branch. They are lost in the woods. They cry out briefly. When they don't touch branches they fly, their legs drawn up to the breast and silent. Kathe doesn't know the name of these birds either.

Kathe searches the cucumber box for a small prickly cucumber. She bites into it with her sharp teeth and spits out the peel.

The sun drops behind the highest hill. The hill wavers and swallows the light. At home the sun is going down behind the cemetery, I say. Kathe eats a big tomato and says: in the mountains night comes earlier than by us at home. Kathe places her small white hand on my knee. The car vibrates between Kathe's hand and my skin. And in the mountains winter comes earlier than by us at home, I say.

The car chugs with green lights through the borders of the woods. Ferns throw their lacy webs into darkness. Our aunt rests her cheek on the window pane and sleeps. Father's cigarette glows above the steering wheel.

Night gobbles up the crates on the car, gobbles up the vegetables in the crates. In the hills the smell of tomatoes grows stronger than by us at home. Kathe has no arms and no face. The stroke of her hands is warm on my knee. Kathe's voice sits at my side and speaks from afar. I bite my lips for silence not to lose my mouth in the night.

The car jerks. Father douses the green lights. He climbs out of the car and calls: we're here. The car stands in front of a long house beneath an electric light. The roof of the house is as black as the forest. Our aunt slams the car door and presses a night-shirt into Father's hand. Her crooked finger points into the darkness and she says: the village is up there. I look where she points and see the moon.

Here's the water mill, Kathe says. Father tucks the night-shirt under his arm and hands a key to our aunt. Our aunt unlocks the green house door. Kathe says: the old lady lives up there in the village with her sister.

Our aunt goes behind a black door. Into her room, Father says. He walks up the small wooden steps and closes the trap-door behind him. Kathe and I lie in a narrow bed below the small black window with white lace curtains. Water rushes through the wall. Kathe says: it's the brook.

Kathe's hair rustles in my ear. At the small black window the moon hangs in the dark jaw of clouds. There the village lies.

Kathe's thighs lie deeper than my thighs. Kathe's head lies higher than my head. Kathe's belly breathes hot air. Beneath my short small body straw cackles.

Behind the black door the bed creaks. Behind the trap-door hay crackles.

The hot air from Kathe's belly smells of rotten pears. Kathe's breath purrs in her sleep. Out of the white lace curtains huge clusters of flowers grow with grasping stems, with looping leaves.

A squeak runs down the steps. I raise my head and let it drop again. Father follows the squeak. Father's barefoot. His large hands finger the black door. The door does not squeak. Father's toes crack and the lock on the black door closes quietly behind his back. Our aunt giggles and says: cold feet. Father smacks his lips and says: mice and hay. The bed creaks. The pillow takes a loud breath. The cover tumbles over in long jolts. Our aunt moans.

Father wheezes. The bed draws away from the wood in short jerks.

Behind the house the brook gurgles. Pebbles push, the stones press. Kathe's hand jerks in her sleep. Our aunt giggles, Father whispers. Behind the black window a round leaf flutters.

The lock on the black door snaps. Father climbs the narrow wooden steps barefooted on his toes. His shirt is open. He smells of rotten pears as he passes. The trap-door squeaks and slowly drops. Kathe turns her face in her sleep. Father's legs crackle in the hay.

The brook gurgles between my eyes. I have done an impure thing, I have looked at an impure thing, I have listened to an impure thing, I have read something impure. I bury my hands under the cover. I draw serpentine roads on my thighs. Our village lies on my knee. Kathe's stomach twitches in her sleep.

The cluster of flowers bend their white stems. The black window has a grey tear. The clouds hang filled with red ties. The fir trees are greening at the needle tips.

Our aunt stands confused in the black doorway. Beneath her night-shirt melons tremble. Our aunt says something about red clouds and wind. At the small window Kathe yawns with her large red mouth and raises her arms. The trap-door squeaks. Father bowed low comes down the narrow steps. His face is stubbly and he says: slept well? I say: yes. Kathe nods. Our aunt buttons her blouse. The button between the melons is too small and pops out of the button-hole. Our aunt looks into Father's face and repeats her sentence about red clouds and wind. Father leans on the wooden steps and combs his hair. He lets a nest of black hair drop from the greasy comb beside the steps. We'll come to get you at two o'clock, he says. Our aunt looks laughing at the green door and says: Kathe knows.

The car hums. Our aunt sits next to Father in the car. She combs her hair with the greasy comb. The hair is grey behind her ears.

I look at the broad red roofs. Kathe says: the village is up there. I ask: is it large? Kathe says: small and ugly.

I lie in the grass. Kathe sits on a stone next to the brook. I see Kathe's blue knickers with the yellow stain of rotten pears between her thighs. Kathe whips the water beneath the stones with a stick.

I look into the water and ask: are you a woman yet? Kathe throws pebbles into the water and says: only those with a husband are women. And your mother, I ask. I chew on a birch leaf in my mouth. Kathe tears at a daisy and recites to herself: loves me, loves me not. Kathe throws the stripped yellow daisy into the water: my mother has children, she says. If you haven't a husband, you don't have children. Where is he, I ask. Kathe turns up a fern: loves me, dead, loves me not. Ask your mother if you don't believe me. I pick daisies. Old Elli doesn't have children, I say. She never had a husband, Kathe says. She smashes a brown spotted frog with a stone. Elli is an old maid, Kathe says. Red hair is inherited. I look into the water. Her chickens are red and her rabbits have red eyes, I say. Small black bugs creep from the daisies over my hand. Elli sings in the garden at night, I say. Kathe stands on a tree stump and cries: she sings because she drinks. Women have to marry so they won't drink. And men, I ask. They drink because they're men, Kathe says and hops into the grass. They stay men even when they don't have wives. And the man you're engaged to, I ask. He drinks because they all drink. And you, I ask. Kathe's eyes roll in her head. I'll get married, she says. I throw a stone into the water and say: I'm not going to drink and I'm not going to marry. Kathe laughs: not now, but later, you're too young now. And if I don't want to, I say. Kathe picks wild strawberries. When you grow up you'll want to, she says.

Kathe lies in the grass eating wild strawberries. Red sand sticks in her teeth. Her legs are long and pale. The spot on Kathe's knickers is wet and dark brown. Kathe throws the empty strawberry stems over her face and sings: and that will bring me someone whom I'll love like no one, and who will give me joy. Her red tongue twists in her mouth and hangs on a white thread. That's what Elli sings in the evening in the garden, I say. Kathe closes her mouth. How does it go on, I ask. Kathe kneels in the grass and waves. The car comes rolling out of the broad roofs. On top of the car empty crates rattle.

Father steps out of the car and locks the green front door. Our aunt sits next to the steering wheel and counts money. Kathe and I climb into the car. The car hums. Kathe sits next to me on an empty cucumber crate.

The car speeds ahead. I see how deep the woods are. Small nameless birds flutter above the road. Pointed shadows of the shrubbery are spotted on Kathe's face. Kathe's lips have sharp dark lines. Her lashes are thick and pointed like pine needles.

There are no men and no women in the village. There are no naked children beneath tall trees. Between tall trees rotten fruit lies. Shaggy dogs bark at our wheels.

The hills pass into wide fields. The plain lies on its black belly. The wind is still. Kathe says: we'll soon be home. She pulls at the drooping chestnut branches. Kathe tears the leaves from the stems with her white hand and has no face. Her voice says softly: loves me, loves me not. Kathe chews the bare stem in her mouth.

Behind the fields there is a grey church steeple: there's our church, Kathe says. The village is flat and black and silent. At the entrance to the village Jesus hangs on a cross, bows his head and shows his hands. His toes are lean and long. Kathe takes a swipe at the cross.

The pond gleams black and empty. In the mill the large snake eats bran and flour. The village is empty. The car stops at the church. I cannot see the steeple. I see the long buckling walls behind the poplar trees.

Kathe walks with our aunt down the black street. The street goes nowhere. I don't see the pavement. I sit next to Father. The seat is still warm with our aunt's thighs and smells of rotten pears.

Father drives and drives. His hand drives through his hair, his tongue over his lips. Father drives with hand and feet through the empty village.

Behind a window without a house a light swings. Father drives through the gate's shadow into the yard. He draws the tarpaulin over the car.

Mother sits at the edge of the table beneath the light. She darns a sock without a heel with grey wool. The wool slides smoothly from her hand. Mother sends a hard-edged look at Father's coat. She smiles. Her smile is weak and hangs at the edge of her mouth.

Father spreads blue paper money on the table and counts. Ten thousand, he says. And my sister, Mother asks. Father says: she's got hers. And the engineer gets eight thousand. Mother asks: from this? Father shakes his head. Mother takes the money in both hands and carries it to the cupboard.

I lie in my bed. Mother bends down and kisses my cheek. Her lips are hard as her fingers. How did you sleep down there, she asks. I close my eyes: Father at the top in the hay, our aunt in her room and Kathe and I in the front room, I say. Mother briefly kisses my brow. Her eyes glow coldly. She turns around and goes away.

The clock ticks in the room: I have listened to an impure thing. My bed rests between a shallow stream and a tired bed of leaves on the plain. Behind the wall the bed creaks with short jerks. Mother moans. Father wheezes. The plain is cluttered with black beds and rotten pears.

Mother's skin is flabby. The pores are empty. The rotten pears crawl back into the skin. Sleep lies black beneath the lids.

Herta Müller
EULOGY

Translated by Agnes Stein

At the station relatives ran alongside the steaming train. With each step their raised arms moved and they winked. A young man stood at the train window. The pane came up to his arms. He held a bouquet of white frazzled flowers at his chest. His face was frozen.

A young woman carried a limp child out of the station. The woman had a hump.

The train drove into the war.

I turned off the television.

Father lay in a coffin in the middle of the room. There were so many pictures hanging one could not see the wall. On one picture Father was half as tall as the chair he clutched. He had on a dress and stood on crooked legs with many folds of fat. His head was pear-shaped and bare.

On another picture Father was the bridegroom. Only half his chest was visible. The other half was a bunch of white frazzled flowers which Mother held in her hand. Their heads were so closely joined the ear lobes touched. On another picture Father stood straight as a stick at a fence. Snow lay beneath the high shoes. The snow was so white Father stood in empty space. His hand was raised above his head in a greeting. Runic characters ran along his collar.

Next to this picture Father held a hoe over his shoulder. behind him the corn stalks reached to the sky. Father had a hat on his head. The hat cast a broad shadow and hid Father's face.

On the next picture Father sat at the steering wheel of a lorry. The lorry was loaded with cattle. Every week Father drove cattle to the slaughter-house in the city.

Father's face was small with sharp edges.

In all the pictures Father was frozen in the middle of a gesture.

In all the pictures Father looked as if he did not know how to go on. But Father always went on. That was why all these pictures were false. With all these false pictures and all these false faces the room had grown cold. I wanted to get off the chair but my dress was fast frozen to the wood. My dress was transparent and black. When I moved it rustled. I got up and touched Father's face. It was colder than the objects in the room. Outside it was summer. Flies dropped dung in flight. The village stretched out beyond the wide sandy path. It was hot and brown and the gleam burned one's eyes.

The cemetery was made of gravel. Large stones lay on the graves.

As I looked down I saw my shoes with the soles turned up. The whole time I had been walking on my boot laces. They lay long and wide behind me. At the ends they curled into each other.

Two small reeling men lifted the coffin from the hearse and lowered it into the grave on two worn ropes. The coffin rocked. Their arms and the ropes grew steadily longer. Despite the drought the grave was filled with water.

Your father had a lot of dead men on his conscience, said one of the drunken little men.

I said: He was in the war. For every 25 dead men he received an award of merit. He brought home several awards.

In a turnip field he raped a woman, the little man said. Together with four other soldiers. Your father stuck a turnip between her legs. When we went away, she bled. She was a Russian. For many weeks afterwards we called all weapons turnips.

It was late fall the little man said. The turnip leaves were black and shrivelled with frost.

Then the little man placed a heavy stone on the coffin. The other little drunk kept on talking: At the New Year we went to the opera in a German town. The soprano sang as shrilly as the Russian had screamed. One by one we left the hall. Your father stayed till the end. For weeks afterwards he called all songs turnips and all women turnip.

The little man drank Schnaps. It gurgled in his stomach. I've got as much Schnaps in my belly as there is ground water in the graves, the little man said.

Then the little man placed a heavy stone on the coffin. The funeral speaker stood next to the white marble cross. He came towards me. He had both hands buried in his coat pockets. The speaker had a rose the size of a hand in his buttonhole. It was velvety. Standing next to me he pulled a hand out of his coat pocket. It was a fist. He wanted to straighten the fingers but he couldn't. His eyes were bulging with pain. He began to cry softly to himself.

You can't get anywhere with country folk in the war, he said. They won't obey orders.

Then the speaker placed a heavy stone on the coffin.

Now a heavy man stood next to me. He had a head like a water-hose and no face.

For years your father slept with my wife, he said. He got me drunk in the boozer and stole my money.

He sat himself down on a stone.

Then a skinny wizened woman came towards me, spat on the ground and said *pfui* to me.

The funeral mourners stood at the other end of the grave. I looked down at myself and was shocked because they could see my breasts. I froze.

All eyes were on me. They were empty. The pupils pierced the lids. The men had rifles slung over their shoulders, and the women rustled with their rosaries.

The speaker pulled at his rose. He tore off a blood-red petal and ate it.

He signalled me with his hand. I knew I now had to make a speech. Everyone looked at me. Not a word came to me. My eyes rose through my throat up to my head. I put my hand to my mouth and bit the fingers. On the back of my hand tooth marks could be seen. My teeth were hot. From the corners of my mouth blood ran to my shoulders.

The wind had torn a sleeve from my dress. Puffed and black

it floated in the air.

A man leaned his walking stick against a heavy stone. He raised his rifle and shot down the sleeve. When it dropped in front of my face it was full of blood. The mourners clapped approval.

My arm was bare. I felt it becoming stone in the air. The speaker made a sign. The clapping stopped.

We are proud of our community. Our fitness keeps us from decline. We won't let them call us names. In the name of our German community you are sentenced to die.

They all pointed their guns at me. In my head there was a deafening bang.

I fell over but did not reach bottom. I remained lying diagonally over their heads in the air. Softly I pushed open the doors.

My mother had cleaned out all the rooms.

In the room where the body had lain on its bier, there was now a long table. It was a butcher's counter. On it stood an empty white plate and a bouquet of white frazzled flowers.

Mother wore a transparent black dress. She held a large knife in her hand. Mother stepped to the mirror and chopped off her thick gray braid with a knife. With both hands she carried it to the table. She placed one end of it on the plate.

I shall wear black the rest of my life, she said.

She lit the braid at one end. It stretched from one end of the table to the other. The braid burned like a fuse. The fire licked and ate.

They sent me to Russia. That was the lightest punishment, she said. I reeled with hunger. At night I crept into a turnip field. The watchman had a gun. If he had seen me he would have killed me. The field did not rustle. It was late fall and the turnip leaves were black and shrivelled.

I no longer saw Mother. The braid was still burning. The room was full of smoke.

They've killed you, my mother said.

We no longer saw each other for the smoke in the room. I heard her step close to me. My outstretched arms reached out to feel for her.

Suddenly she hooked her bony hand in my hair. She shook my head. I screamed.

I tore my eyes open. The room was turning around. I lay in a ball of white frazzled flowers and was locked inside.

Then I had the feeling the block of flats was turned over and emptying into the ground.

The alarm clock rang. It was Saturday morning, 5.30 a.m.

James Purdy
KITTY BLUE

Many years ago in a far distant country, there was a famous opera singer who was very fond of cats. She found her greatest inspiration in talking with her cats both before and after she sang in grand opera houses. Without the encouragement and love of these gifted beasts she felt she would never understand the various roles she interpreted on the opera stage. Her only sorrow was that very often a favourite cat would die or disappear or sometimes even be stolen by a person who was envious of her.

Madame Lenore, the opera singer, was admired by the crown prince who at the time of this story was only fifteen years old. He never missed a single one of Madame Lenore's performances and showered her with costly gifts, and after one of her appearances he saw to it that the stage was piled high with the most expensive and exotic flowers.

One day the crown prince learned that Madame Lenore had lost the last of her favourite cats. The prince immediately decided to send her a new one, but he knew this one should be not only the most beautiful cat in his kingdom but the brightest and most gifted.

The prince scoured his realm looking for a cat worthy of so eminent a singer. He went to over a hundred shops in his search. At long last he found the cat he was looking for in an out-of-the-way bazaar run by a young Abyssinian youth named Abdullah. Abdullah pointed out to his majesty that although the cat he presented to the prince was only a few months old, it already displayed extraordinary mental powers, and under his careful tutelage could speak fluently in human language.

The prince was carried away with enthusiasm for his find,

and immediately struck a bargain to purchase so splendid a puss.

"There is only one thing I must warn you of, your majesty," Abdullah said as the prince was about to leave with his purchase. "This cat must not be allowed to keep company with other ordinary cats, but he must remain always close to his human owner and guardian. For in my opinion, he is only a cat in his exterior, his soul is that of a higher being."

The prince was even more delighted with this new information from Abdullah, and he promised he would obey the instructions to the letter, and with that he set out with the gifted cat.

On their way to the palace, the prince was suddenly dumbfounded to hear the cat speaking to him in a soft but clear and unaffected voice.

"My prince, my name is Kitty Blue," the cat began, "and I am honoured that you should wish to adopt me into your royal household. You may depend, your majesty, on my always being a faithful subject who will never disappoint you or leave your royal company."

"Thank you, Kitty Blue. I am most touched by what you say," the young prince replied. "But unfortunately," he stammered, "unfortunately..."

"Unfortunately what?" the cat enquired, for he saw his royal owner was upset. "Please tell me what is worrying you."

"Dear Kitty Blue, the fact is that I have promised you to another."

"To another!" Kitty Blue raised his voice. "How can that be?"

"I promised you, dear friend, to the most beautiful and most talented opera singer of our day: Madame Lenore."

The cat said nothing, and the prince saw that the gifted creature was deeply hurt that the prince had promised him to someone else.

"I cannot very well go back on my promise, can I?" the prince spoke in anguished tones.

"I suppose not, your highness," the cat said hesitantly. "But it will be hard to leave your royal presence even for so gifted and beautiful a person as Madame Lenore."

"But I will always be near you, Kitty Blue, and you can always call on me at any hour. Remember that."

The prince noticed a few tears falling from the cat's wonderfully blue eyes, and he remembered that Kitty Blue had the name he was known by because of the beautiful blue colour of his eyes.

Hugging the cat to him, the prince tried to comfort his unusual pet with many sweet words, but he saw, alas, that nothing he said could console the cat for having to leave his royal protection and company.

The next day the prince summoned Madame Lenore to the palace to receive the gift he had promised her.

It was a beautiful June evening. The odour of jasmine was in the air, and the sky was a cloudless blue over which songbirds flew in countless numbers, and the many trees surrounding the palace stirred in a faint breeze.

Madame Lenore came accompanied by a young attendant who was extremely devoted to the famous singer, and who almost never left her side.

The prince forbade Madame Lenore to bow to him.

"You are the sovereign here this evening," the prince said and took her hand in his, "and I shall bow to you."

When they had all taken their seats, the prince slowly began speaking.

"I have a gift for you, dear singer," the prince informed her. "A gift such as I myself would be thrilled to accept for my own."

He clapped his hands, and an attendant brought in a great silver box with tiny windows the top and sides of which sparkled with precious gems.

"Kitty Blue," the prince said, rising. "Will you now come forth, and meet your new mistress."

"I will, my prince," a small but clear voice resounded. And Kitty Blue, attired in a handsome suit with small diamond buttons emerged from the box and immediately after bowing to the crown prince advanced toward Madame Lenore and said in perfectly articulated tones, "Good evening, esteemed Madame Lenore."

Madame Lenore was so overcome with surprise and joy at

hearing so beautiful a cat address her that she came close to fainting. Immediately a servant brought her a glittering glass of refreshment which she quaffed quickly and so regained her composure.

Kitty Blue then leaped into her lap and, looking up into her eyes, exclaimed: "You are just as beautiful and charming as the whole world says you are."

"How can I ever thank you, my lord," Madame Lenore cried, turning to the prince. "You have given me the one gift I have longed for day and night."

There was all at once a clarion call of brass instruments summoning the prince to leave so that he rose hurriedly and kissed the singer's hand by way of leave-taking.

He then turned to Kitty Blue. "Be good and considerate, Kitty Blue, to your new mistress, for no one except myself will love you so devotedly. But should you ever need anything, remember I too am your loving friend."

Having said this the prince bowed low to the wonderful cat and his new mistress and then surrounded all at once by his guards left the room.

Just before he got into his horse-drawn carriage the prince remembered the warning of Abdullah and he wrote out a note which he asked one of his attendants to hurry back and give to the singer.

The note read:

Under no circumstances, dear Madame Lenore, are you to permit Kitty Blue to associate with common cats. He must speak only to persons such as ourselves.

The Crown Prince.

Madame Lenore read the prince's note carefully several times and afterwards put it away in one of her voluminous pockets. But she was still so captivated by the gift of the wonderful cat the prince's message of warning soon slipped her mind.

Madame Lenore had never known such a devoted companion as she found in Kitty Blue. Because of his fluency in speaking, there was no subject on which she could not converse with him. He asked a thousand questions about her life and her career as a singer.

They often spoke far into the night, and fell asleep together in the singer's sumptuous four-poster bed. If Madame Lenore awoke during the night and did not find Kitty Blue by her side, she would call out to him and then to her relief and joy she would find him at only an arm's length away from her.

Madame Lenore began taking Kitty Blue with her to the opera house. He would wait patiently in her dressing room during the performance of the music drama, and during the intermission the two of them would confer lengthily.

The public and the singer's countless admirers had never remembered her to sing so beautifully or look so stunning as she interpreted her various operatic roles.

It was indeed a new Madame Lenore who appeared before the operatic stage.

The singer gave full credit to Kitty Blue for her resurgence and she was not ashamed to tell her manager and the conductor of the orchestra that it was Kitty Blue who often coached her in her interpretation of her roles.

She was at the acme of her happiness.

One day an invitation came from the ruling monarch of Constantinople requesting the favour of her appearing in a series of private performances at the royal court. She was about to accept so important an invitation when she learned from an official of the court that she could not bring any pets or animals.

"But Kitty Blue is not a pet or an animal," she spoke to the delegate of the King.

But the delegate was adamant.

At first Madame Lenore declined the invitation, but Kitty Blue then spoke up to her. "Madame Lenore, your career is your life, and you must go to Constantinople without me. I will be waiting for you here and you will be gone in any case only a few days or a week or so at the most."

But Madame Lenore could not be consoled. She wept and sobbed, and kept repeating that she could not stand to be without her tried and true companion Kitty Blue.

Finally, at the insistence of her manager and the representative of the royal court of Constantinople she made the hard decision and agreed to go.

She entrusted Kitty Blue to her faithful attendant beseeching him to look after her prized and beloved cat.

Their parting was heart-breaking for both the singer and the marvellous cat, and Madame Lenore had almost to be carried out to the ship waiting in the harbour.

Kitty Blue was if possible even more unhappy without the companionship and love of Madame Lenore than the great singer was without her wonderful cat. The young man who was to keep him company, Jack Morfey, treated Kitty Blue kindly but only as he would any cat, seldom spoke to him and never sang to him as did Madame Lenore. True, Jack fed him excellent meals, brushed his fur and changed his suits often three times a day, but otherwise ignored him.

One day in his lonesomeness, Kitty Blue observed that off the large drawing room was a great window overlooking a spacious garden. From then on the cat took his position always in front of the window to gaze longingly out at all the trees and flowering plants and the butterflies and birds flying endlessly across the sky. He was almost happy then.

Because of his sitting in front of the window so many hours he attracted the attention of a great monarch of a cat who considered himself in fact the king of the garden.

One day Great Cat strode up to the big window and addressed Kitty Blue: "What are you doing here so close to my garden?" he enquired, and he flashed his coal-black eyes with indignation.

Now Kitty Blue had never spoken with a cat before, for he had learned only human language, so for a moment he was not sure what Great Cat was saying, but being so bright he soon deduced what his visitor had said.

"I am Kitty Blue, sir, friend and companion to Madame Lenore, the famous diva."

Great Cat was nearly as bright as Kitty Blue, and he soon had figured out what Kitty Blue was saying in human language.

"I see," Great Cat spoke in a slightly sneering tone. "Well, you certainly have on pretty clothes, don't you, and ribbons besides, and is that by chance a jewel in your left ear?"

Kitty Blue nodded and looked wistfully out at all the trees, flowers, butterflies and dragonflies.

"Would you care to take a stroll in my garden?" Great Cat spoke coaxingly.

"I am forbidden to leave this room, Great Cat."

"By whom are you forbidden, may I ask?" his visitor wondered contemptuously.

"By the crown prince."

Great Cat showed utter indifference for this explanation.

"Kitty Blue, think what you are missing. Look out way over there," Great Cat said, pointing with his paw to a wildflower garden in the rear of the garden proper. "Have you ever seen anything so beautiful? And you want to stay cooped up in this stuffy room because some prince says you must! When we cats all know royalty don't give a hoot about us and in the first place the prince has given you away to Madame Lenore, and Madame Lenore herself can't care too much about you since she has gone gallivanting off to Constantinople leaving you behind."

Kitty Blue was so pained by this last remark that two fat tears dropped from his very blue eyes.

"See here, Blue," Great Cat said, "supposing I come by here tomorrow at ten o'clock and by then maybe you will have made up your mind to visit my garden. Toodle-oo!"

And Great Cat having given this speech rose loftily and without another word departed.

Kitty Blue could not think of anything but the words of Great Cat, and though he tried to speak with Jack Morfey, Jack paid little or no attention to what Kitty Blue said. Jack confined his attentions to serving Kitty his meals punctually and changing his costumes every few hours. (He had a morning costume, an afternoon costume and finally a sumptuous evening-wear suit.)

The forlorn cat kept looking out at the beautiful garden all that day and all evening too, and when night came instead of going to his bedchamber he lay in front of the window and watched the stars come out in the eastern sky as a lazy red moon rose over the sycamore trees.

He made up his mind then and there that he would accept

51

Great Cat's invitation and go for a stroll with him in the garden.

True to Great Cat's promise, he arrived the next day punctually at ten o'clock.

"Well, what is your decision?" Great Cat said in an offhand and curt manner. "Are you coming with me to the garden or aren't you?"

"I would like very much to, but isn't the window tight bolted?" Kitty Blue said anxiously.

"What's bolted can always be unbolted," Great Cat responded, and putting all his considerable weight against the window pane he pushed it wide open.

"Coming?" Great Cat spoke in a scolding tone.

Kitty Blue cast one look behind him at his room and the different velvet cushions on which he reclines, and then with a sigh followed Great Cat out into the immense outdoors.

Kitty Blue could not help exclaiming about the marvellous variety of things the garden had to offer. He had never seen such an abundance of trees, shrubs and climbing vines, or so many birds, chipmunks, and bluejays and crows.

"And beyong the garden, Kitty Blue, are even more wonderful things waiting for you! Why you want to live in that old house crowded with antique furniture, bric-a-brac and thick dusty carpets I will never know."

Great Cat then proceeded to give the younger cat a complete and comprehensive tour, pointing out all the different varieties of trees, bushes, creeping vines and flowers, and drawing attention to the many grey squirrels and last of all to a number of huge crows who watched the two cats with extreme suspicion. And all around them there was a constant moving circle of butterflies, dragonflies and small twittering wrens.

"Excuse me a moment, Kitty Blue," Great Cat said suddenly. "I see a friend over there near the tulip tree, who I am sure would like to meet you. Stay here until I speak with him."

Great Cat rushed over to the edge of the garden where a grey tomcat with only one eye and massive jaws and paws had been observing them.

Kitty Blue watched with considerable uneasiness as the two

large cats spoke together. From time to time they would both look over in his direction and grin.

All at once Kitty Blue heard someone call him by name. Looking up toward a rhododendron bush he caught sight of a very pretty mourning dove who now addressed him: "Kitty Blue, if you know what is good for you, return at once to Madame Lenore's house. You are keeping the worst possible company by coming out here with Great Cat and his friend One Eye. They are both bad actors and will get you into plenty of trouble if you are not careful. Mark my words."

The mourning dove then flew up to the roof of an adjoining church where his mate was waiting for him.

Kitty Blue was so frightened by the dove's warning that he hurried back to Madame Lenore's house, but not only was the window now tightly closed but an enormous shutter had been placed over the window preventing entry.

All at once a strong even melodious voice said: "So you are the Kitty Blue we have all been hearing about."

A young man dressed as if for a pageant, wearing a high hat and a feathered vest, with rings on almost all his fingers, was addressing the unhappy cat.

Kitty Blue had barely enough strength to say Yes.

Great Cat and One Eye now also approached and began speaking, but the young man severely warned them to be quiet and better still to be off.

"You alley cats have served your purpose, now skidoo!" he cried. Both Great Cat and One Eye made a great caterwauling until the young mountebank (for this is what he was) threw them several helpings of catnip, which the cats greedily seized before running off into the bushes.

"Let me introduce myself, Kitty Blue," the young man said, and all at once he took hold of Kitty Blue and sitting down on a bench held him in his lap. "My name is Kirby Jericho," he said, "and I am a long-time friend of your mistress, Madame Lenore. I happened by chance to hear those two alley cats talking about you, for I understand puss language since I am in the pageant and theatre business. They brought me straight to you." As he spoke,

Kirby fondled Kitty Blue gently and then carefully touched him on the ear.

"I don't suppose you noticed, but Great Cat robbed you of your ear-ring and your necklace."

Kitty Blue gave out a short sob when he realised this was true.

"Madame Lenore," Kirby Jericho went on, "has been detained in Constantinople. The young sovereign there has absolutely refused to let her leave for another month or so. Since I am one of her friends of long standing, I am proposing you come and stay with me until she returns. Meantime I want to train you for appearing in the theatre of Herbert of Old Vienna, who is also a former friend of Madame Lenore."

Kitty Blue was so miserable at having been locked out of Madame Lenore's apartment and of being robbed by Great Cat, he barely heard anything Kirby Jericho said to him, but being in desperate mood he reluctantly allowed himself to be persuaded to go with his new protector, for that is what Jericho said he was.

Kitty Blue was considerably surprised to see that a brand new roadster was waiting for them beyond the garden walls.

"Sit in the front, if you please, so we can talk on the way to my studio, if you don't mind," Jericho advised.

Kitty Blue took his place beside Jericho and in one second or two off they went through the lonely deserted streets on the way to the vaudeville and dance theatre, and to what Kitty Blue was later to learn would be a new and entirely different life.

After a while Jericho slowed down and turned to the cat and after stammering badly he managed to get out the following: "Kitty Blue, do you realise the danger you were in, trespassing in Great Cat's garden?"

Kitty Blue was so miserable and unhappy without Madame Lenore he barely heard what Jericho said. Finally, however, he managed to say, "I suppose so."

"I see you don't," Jericho sighed. "But let me tell you another thing. Madame Lenore could not have cared very much about you if she up and left you without anybody to watch over you. No, don't interrupt, don't defend her. She is a fickle woman. On the other hand, if you will come live with me in the Vaudeville and Paradise Theatre, you will find a true home and, what's more, a profession. I will teach you to be a dancer and performer, and a guitar player. Doesn't that sound like the real thing now?"

Kitty Blue nodded, but he was so heartbroken to hear that Madame Lenore was fickle and had deserted him that he burst into tears.

"There, there now," Jericho comforted him and handed him a handkerchief to dry his tears with. Jericho started the motor again and they were soon across the river and into the back streets of a district given over to acrobats, dancers, jugglers and other entertainers.

They drove up to a theatre ablaze with pink and violet lights, and over the front entrance shimmered a great marquee with the words

THE VAUDEVILLE AND MUSIC HALL OF
HERBERT OF OLD VIENNA

"Don't be upset that my name is not in lights," Jericho said, helping Kitty Blue out of his car, "it will be, one day soon, for Herbert is longing to retire. By the way, did you know Madame Lenore got her start in this very vaudeville and music hall? Well, she did, and herbert was her maestro. They quarrelled, of course, and Madame Lenore went on to be a famous diva."

Kitty Blue dried his tears and with a great sigh allowed himself to be ushered in to Herbert of Vienna's vaudeville and music hall theatre.

Madame Lenore's appearance in Constantinople was thought to be a stunning success by everybody except the singer herself and her manager, a young man from Milan who had watched her progress from her early days. "Something was missing," she confided to him one evening as they sat together in their spacious hotel suite. "Don't tell me I was perfect for I was not!"

"Correct me if what I am going to say is wrong," the manager said, "but Madame Lenore, strange as it may seem, you miss Kitty Blue. Being away from him has taken something out of your voice."

Madame Lenore sadly agreed. "How perceptive you are, my

dear friend. Not only do I miss him, but I have had terrible dreams and a presentiment something has happened to him while I have been away."

"I am sure everything is all right with him," her manager replied, "for you left him in the company of your most trusted servant. So don't worry on that score. You are homesick, and homesickness is one of our greatest sorrows."

Madame Lenore tried now to look on the bright side, but she noted again the next evening that her voice, despite the rapturous applause greeting her, was lacking in a certain strength and conviction. She knew then how much she loved Kitty Blue and that she could not be happy without him.

After her performance that evening the stage was filled with hundreds of large bouquets and wreaths of flowers of every kind, but their perfume and beauty failed to touch the singer's heart and her eyes were streaming with tears.

All the way back on the ship she could think of nothing but Kitty Blue and his amazing gift of speaking to her in her own language.

"As soon as I set eyes on him," she told her manager, "my heart will be lifted up and then, you see, my voice will again have all its former resonance and power."

The next day they arrived home, and Madame Lenore flung open the door with fervent expectation, and called out the name of the cat. The young attendant appeared immediately. As she looked at his troubled face, Madame Lenore's worst suspicions stirred in her mind.

"What is your news?" she enquired in a chilled weak voice.

"Madame Lenore," the attendant began as he helped her off with her coat, "something very upsetting has occurred."

"Is it Kitty Blue?"

He nodded. "Kitty Blue has disappeared," he explained. "We have made every effort to locate him, but he has left without a trace except for the little scarf which he sometimes wore around his neck. This we found in the garden outside." And the attendant produced the scarf, which was the same colour as the eyes of the cat.

Madame Lenore lay back in her chair, closed her eyes, and shook with choking sobs.

All kinds of dire fears and suspicions tormented Madame Lenore's mind. After realising Kitty Blue had disappeared without the least clue to where he had gone, the great singer took to her bed, refused food and lived on iced water and an occasional glass of champagne. Within two weeks she had lost so much weight and was so frail she could scarcely rise from her sumptuous four-poster. She cancelled all her appearances, to the anger and bitter disappointment of the great Gatti Cazzasa, the director of the opera house.

Against the advice of her manager and her friends, she summoned many world-famous detectives. Only the enormous amount of money the singer promised them prevailed upon the detectives to take a case involving the disappearance of a cat, despite the fact that the cat had been the gift of the crown prince himself.

One of the detectives who listened to her story was a more humane and benevolent man than his colleagues, who had merely taken huge sums of the singer's money and produced no results.

The detective, named Nello Gambini, listened quietly as Madame Lenore poured out all her sorrow, together with the few facts she had gathered about Kitty Blue's last days.

"What you need, my dear lady," Nello Gambini finally said, "is not a detective but a seeress."

"A seeress!" Madame Lenore exclaimed, and sat up in her bed for the first time in days. "I think, Signor Gambini, you are absolutely right... but," and her voice quavered, "where on earth can I find a seeress who will not be dishonest and grasping?"

"Ah, but there is one, and only one. The difficulty, however," Signor Gambini said as he accepted a cup of coffee, "the difficulty is that Senora Cleandra no longer will see anybody."

"Then why have you given me her name?" The anguished singer broke into new weeping.

"Listen to me, dear madame," Signor Gambini comforted her, "if I call her she will see you, for I once located her lost diamond necklace."

Madame Lenore smiled.

The famous detective handed her a card with the name and address of the seeress.

Rising, the detective wiped his mouth carefully with a linen napkin and said, "Be sure to tell her that I arranged for you to meet one another and under no circumstances is she to refuse to help you."

Madame Lenore was too ill and weak to go to Senora Cleandra's home, and only after emphasising that it was a matter of life and death did the old fortune-teller agree to visit the singer, though, as Senora Cleandra remarked on the phone, it was against her considered better judgement to leave her own domicile.

Senora Cleandra's appearance was astounding. She was nearly seven feet tall and her hands were laden with jewels and a strong herbal odour emanated from her person. Besides this, she was so heavily veiled from head to foot that one could scarcely see her eyes. She said she would only partake of a raw onion as refreshment, but after chewing thoughtfully on the onion for a while she changed her mind and said she would take a cup of beef broth.

"And now, dear Madame Lenore, tell me what person so beloved of you is missing, and I will attempt to locate him."

"When you say person, dear Senora, you are speaking the truth. Yet I must tell you the loved one whose absence has brought me to my death bed, is a cat..."

Senora Cleandra, hearing who the missing party was, stood up to the full extent of her seven feet and gave out an ear-splitting shriek followed by a volley of curses.

Pray be seated, dear Senora," Madame Lenore begged her.

"You have brought me here to locate a *cat* for you," the seeress cried. "Have you no realisation of what an insult that is to me, the Senora Cleandra who has hitherto only been a consultant to members of royalty and other crowned heads. A cat! Indeed!"

"Dear Senora, listen to me," Madame Lenore whispered, shaking in a fit of trembling. "Though he has, it is true, a cat's body, he is not a cat but a young prince, I am convinced. He speaks the language of aristocracy and not the mewings of an ordinary feline. And he loves me, and I love him. If he does not come back to me, I shall die."

"Have you any spirits in the house?" Senora Cleandra enquired of one of the attendants. "Some eau-de-vie, perhaps," she added.

The servant immediately brought the seeress a snifter of the finest brandy, and after sipping the liquor lengthily, Senora Cleandra lowered her veil and, looking closely at Madame Lenore, said, "If he is not a cat but, as you claim, a prince, then I could extend my services. But first I must have an article the disappeared one often touched - I suppose in his case something he held in his paw."

"Bring the Senora Kitty Blue's velvet breeches," Madame Lenore commanded, and for the first time in weeks the singer rose and painfully walked over to the largest chair in the room.

Madame Lenore was about to add some more information to Senora Cleandra about her missing pet when she saw that the seeress had fallen into a deep trance: her head had leaned to one side and the veils about her face had fallen away to reveal her chin and upper lip covered with a heavy growth of beard.

The seeress then began speaking in a greatly altered voice: "Your beloved Kitty Blue is a prisoner, dear lady, of the notorious live-animal trainer and pantomimist, Herbert of Old Vienna. Kitty Blue was handed over to Herbert by the notorious rapscallion, Kirby Jericho, and your dearly beloved is required to appear nightly as an entertainer and guitarist, and is also forced to dance and perform acrobatics."

Senora Cleandra now opened her eyes and adjusted her veils so that her growth of beard was no longer noticeable. She stared balefully then at Madame Lenore.

"You should eat nothing but rare beef for the next two weeks," she advised the opera singer.

"But where, dear Senora, can I find Herbert of Old Vienna?"

"You, a singer, have never heard of Herbert of Old Vienna? Then I pity you."

Senora Cleandra hurriedly wrote out the showman's address and handed it to the bereaved Lenore.

"How much am I indebted to you for, Senora," Madame Lenore enquired after getting possession of herself and reading again and again the address of Herbert of Old Vienna.

The seeress had moved toward the door. Then turning around she said in a voice as low as that of a bass baritone, "Owe? Are you crazy! Nothing. Do you think I would accept money for locating a cat, whether he is a prince in disguise or maybe a goblin. Senora Cleandra does not receive pay for locating animals."

She opened the door and rushed out.

Weak as she was, Madame Lenore followed after the seeress and cried, "You must have recompense, dear lady. Please come back and accept any gift you may desire."

But Madame Lenore was too late. The heavy outer door had slammed behind the visitor and a cold current of air came out from the street causing Madame Lenore to cough and sneeze.

Madame Lenore was filled with hope on hearing Senora Cleandra's words that Kitty Blue might be found at Herbert of Old Vienna's, but this information also caused her great pain. Madame Lenore now recalled that many years ago she had been a pupil at Herbert of Old Vienna's Ventriloquist and Vaudeville Studio. He had been very fond of her then and she had been his favourite pupil in that long-ago epoch. But they had quarrelled violently because Herbert, who was once world-famous in Vienna, had proposed marriage to Madame Lenore. She had refused his suit, and as a result he had become her bitter enemy. She realised that it would be very difficult to return to the ventriloquist and vaudeville studio, especially when her coming was to beg the favour of returning Kitty Blue to her. But Madame Lenore was now only too aware that unless she could find Kitty Blue again, she would never recover her health or her operatic career.

Herbert of Old Vienna had already been alerted by Senora Cleandra that Madame Lenore would be coming to his studio and would attempt to abduct Kitty Blue.

Although the singer was heavily disguised the evening she paid her call to the Vaudeville Theatre, she knew that Herbert, who was also clairvoyant, would spot her even if she appeared as a bundle of brooms.

Nonetheless she took her courage in her hands and boldly walked into the small theatre and sat in a prominent place near the stage.

A young man dressed in lemon-coloured tights was juggling what appeared to be a hundred brightly-coloured balls, but of course clever use of lights had made one ball appear many. It was easy to believe that the young man was throwing countless balls in the air and catching every one with more ease than the best trained seal.

He bowed to Madame Lenore at the end of his act and blew her several kisses.

Next a young girl dressed as a mermaid appeared and again through Herbert's clever use of lights she gave the illusion that she was swimming in a beautiful green sea. She too recognised Madame Lenore and bowed low after her act.

Giuseppe Fellorini, the Strong Man of Herbert's troop, now came thundering out. He raised one heavy object after another in his brawny arms, including what looked like a grand piano and a Fat Lady reputed to weigh 500 pounds. He was too proud of his strength, however, to bow to Madame Lenore and would barely look at her, but instead he blew kisses to the audience which was applauding him fervently.

Then the lights dimmed, and soft if slightly sad music from the cello and harp sounded. Madame Lenore knew her prince was about to appear, and she had to reach for her smelling bottle to keep from fainting.

Kitty Blue, dressed in a suit of mother of pearl and diamonds, came forward with a guitar. He did not seem to recognise Madame Lenore at first, and began strumming his guitar and then sang the famous words:

In your sweet-scented garden I lost my way. Your window once full of light Closed forever against my beating heart I lost my way because you had gone away.

But here Kitty Blue's paws trembled and his voice became choked. He had recognised Madame Lenore. He rose from the shining silver chair in which he was seated and cried out: "Madame Lenore, is it after all you? Tell me what I see is true."

James Purdy

Madame Lenore could not contain herself. She rose from her own seat and rushed upon the stage. The cat and the great singer embraced and kissed one another and burst into tears.

"You must come home with me at once, dear Blue," Madame Lenore managed to get these words out.

But at that moment they heard a terrifying voice of such volume that the chandeliers of the small theatre vibrated and shook.

"You shall do nothing of the sort, Madame Lenore - for it is you, isn't it? Take your hands off my star performer, and you, Kitty Blue, go to your dressing room!"

It was of course Herbert of Old Vienna.

"How dare you interrupt a performance here!" he shouted in the most terrible rage Madame Lenore could recall.

But she was no longer the cringing young pupil she had been in Herbert's vaudeville and burlesque house.

Madame Lenore almost spat at the great ventriloquist as she cried, "Kitty Blue is mine, not yours. He was a gift from the crown prince and you have no claim on him."

"If you so much as touch this cat," Herbert shouted in an even louder tone, "I shall have both you and him arrested and sent to the Island. You are in my theatre, and furthermore you are still facing charges for having run out on me years ago, owing me thousands of pounds sterling and gold guineas. And once you are jailed you shall stay there till you are turned to dust!"

"Jail me? You shall do nothing of the sort, you low mountebank," Madame Lenore cried.

Because she was living in a dangerous city, Madame Lenore always carried a pearl-handled pistol. And so she drew out this pistol from one of the voluminous folds of her gown.

Now Herbert of Old Vienna had an almost demented fear of firearms, possibly because both his third and fourth wives had shot him, seriously wounding him.

When he saw Madame Lenore levelling the gun at him, he fell on his knees and burst into an unmanly series of sobs.

Still holding the gun in his direction, Madame Lenore, walking backwards, reached the stage door and then the dressing room. She found Kitty Blue hiding under a player-piano. Kitty Blue hearing the singer's voice rushed into her arms.

They hurried into the back part of the theatre and went out to the stage door, where fortuitously one of the horse-drawn carriages was waiting for the Strong Man. They jumped in and as Madame Lenore was still holding her pearl-handled pistol the driver was too terrified not to obey her and started in the direction of the singer's palatial residence.

Herbert had recovered partially from his fear and raced out after them, but at this point Madame Lenore fired her pistol in the air and when the mountebank heard the gunfire he fell in a dead faint to the pavement thinking he had been shot.

The carriage was soon rushing away and within minutes had reached the residence of the famed opera singer.

Exhausted from his ordeal, Kitty Blue was easily persuaded to be ensconced in his comfortable place in Madame Lenore's four-poster, but sleep was out of the question. And the singer was avid to hear of the cat's adventures.

But before he could begin, the new servants - Madame Lenore had dismissed all her former help on the grounds that they had neglected the safety and person of Kitty Blue - brought his favourite dessert of candied devilled shrimp and strawberries in brandy and anise cream.

He had barely begun to enjoy the repast when all the doors of the chamber were flung open and in strode the crown prince who had got wind of the rescue of the cat.

The prince was nearly as overcome with joy as his friend the opera singer, and they all embraced one another in an excess of joyful thanksgiving.

"He was just beginning to tell me how it was he was lost to us," Madame Lenore told the prince.

"I had forgotten, Your Grace," Kitty Blue turned to His Highness, "that I was forbidden to talk with common cats."

"And from what I have heard," the prince said, "you could hardly have chosen a worse creature to speak to than the notorious Great Cat and his accomplice, One Eye, who I am glad to tell you have both been sent to prison for life."

Kitty Blue could not help smiling.

"After Great Cat had robbed me of my ear-ring, I was rescued by a young theatre scout sent to locate promising talent by Herbert of Old Vienna."

"And don't I know the theatre scout you mention," the prince was indignant. "Kirby Jericho is his name."

Kitty Blue nodded. "He took me to his training chamber," the cat went on, "and for six weeks I was his prisoner while he coached me and instrucrted me in the art of guitar playing, elocution and soft-shoe dancing, prior to his turning me over to Herbert of Old Vienna."

The prince could not help interrupting the narrative here by cries of outrage.

Madame Lenore cringed at the thought of what her beloved cat had suffered in her absence.

Despite his painful adventures, and the accompanying pain and suffering they had inflicted on Kitty Blue, both Madame Lenore and the prince had to admit that the cat's experiences had given him, if possible, an even more ingratiating and splendid personality, and, what is more, an almost inexhaustible repertory.

"Before, dear Blue," the prince expressed it this way, "you were a marvellous companion and a sterling intimate, but having been trained by wicked but brilliant Herbert of Old Vienna and Kirby Jericho, you are without an equal in the entire world."

The prince then stood up and folded his arms.

"I want to invite you, Madame Lenore, and Kitty Blue, to accompany me on an ocean cruise around the world beginning tomorrow at noon. Will you kindly accept such an invitation?"

As he waited for their reply, the prince added:

"I think both of you could stand with a long vacation, and this one is scheduled to last for seventeen months."

Madame Lenore turned to her favourite cat for a response.

Kitty Blue fairly leaped for joy at the thought of a world cruise with a royal protector and the greatest living singer, and nodded acceptance.

And so the three of them became during that long sea voyage inseparable friends and companions. And almost every night, at the prince's command, Kitty Blue would entertain them with the story of his adventures, interspersed with his guitar playing and singing and soft-shoe routine, and his narrative of his adventures changing a little from night to night, new details coming into the story, new additions not imparted before, gave the prince and Madame Lenore such entertainment that they never knew a dull moment on their sea voyage, and the three of them became the most famous trio perhaps known then or thereafter.

JAMES PURDY
"An authentic American genius" - Gore Vidal

OUT WITH THE STARS (£14.95 h/b, £7.95 p/b)
"Oddly compelling and lushly enjoyable... a highly coloured, utterly
unbelievable and enjoyable book"
The Spectator

ON GLORY'S COURSE (£13.50)
"I read *On Glory's Course* with gusto. The text seems even richer than usual and
is wonderfully satisfying"
Paul Bowles

MOURNERS BELOW (£13.50)
"Purdy is a master of the horrible, the wildly funny and the very sad"
Angus Wilson

THE CANDLE OF YOUR EYES (£13.50)
"A writer of the highest rank in originality, insight and power"
Dorothy Parker

IN THE HOLLOW OF HIS HAND (£13.50)
"Fantastic talent. His books take one by the throat and shake one's bones
loose. The American language at its best"
George Steiner

GARMENTS THE LIVING WEAR (£12.95)
"He will surely enchant the reader who values a new expression of feeling and
experience"
Tennessee Williams

THE HOUSE OF THE SOLITARY MAGGOT (£13.95)
"Unquestionably one of the best writers in America"
Fran Lebowitz

Peter Owen Publishers, 73 Kenway Road, London SW5 0RE
(071-373-5628)

Vladislav Bajac
THE BOOK OF BAMBOO

Translated from Serbo-Croat
by Christine Pribicevic Zoric

PART ONE

I.

Obuto Nissan got dressed and set out on his morning inspection of the master's groves. He had a habit of talking to himself while walking, accustomed as he was to the solitude he had lived in for so many years. He had decided not to mix with other people unless absolutely necessary a few months after marrying his betrothed, on the day of her death. That entire year the plague had ravaged the province and all that Nissan could understand was that human misery was infinite. When he realized that fate was not about to claim his life, he applied to the daimyo Bonzon to serve as keeper of the most remote bamboo groves on Mount Shito. For a full thirty years since then, Nissan had not come down from the mountain. His only human contact was once every few months when one of the Zen priests from the Dabou-ji temple would stop on his pilgrimage to rest at Nissan's hut.

His salary, along with news from the empire, was brought to him once a year by one of the master's supervisors, the samurai Ishi. Appearing with him, during the bamboo cutting season, would be labourers heading back for their distant homes once the job was done, but not a word did they exchange with Nissan. He spent his time in the company of the tall reeds whose very soul he felt he knew.

That particular morning a special task awaited him; he took his tools to cut down the biggest stalk on the plantation, as ordered by supervisor Ishi. The tall bamboo seemed to resist, Nissan had to use all his strength to fell it. A few hours later, the bamboo lay at his feet. Tired, Nissan sat on the trunk, staring at the endless lines of troops under his command. It was often his custom to talk to his soldiers.

This time in response to one of his questions there came a muffled sound from the trunk on which he was sitting. Certain that it was his imagination, for he knew the answers to his questions, Nissan slowly stood up, bent his ear toward the sound and repeated the question. When he heard a distinct tapping from inside the stalk, he jumped aside in fright.

"Some animal must be inside. But how did it get in there?" Nissan wondered aloud.

"That I won't tell you, but help me get out of here," a reedy, clear voice replied.

Nissan leaped into the air and ran behind the nearest big bamboo stalk. From there he gaped at what was happening before his very eyes.

Out of the stalk crawled a child, it stood up and motioned him over. Nissan's eyes opened wide in disbelief. He remained riveted to the spot. The little girl said to him: "I'm not afraid of you. Why don't you come over here to me?"

Nissan collected himself and stepped toward her. Still standing at a safe distance, he asked her: "Who are you?"

"My name is Kaguyahime. I've got nobody and I've come to live with you, if you'll have me."

"But where have you come from?" Nissan asked, gaining a bit more time to think.

"Why, you saw. From the bamboo."

"Hmm. You'll tell me later." He had decided. "I'll take you in as my daughter." Then, without a word, he finished the job he had begun, while Kaguyahime looked on in silence.

They set off together for Nissan's hut. On the way the little girl clasped his hand. He observed her out of the corner of his eye, his step almost proud. Until now, no one had ever asked for his protection, let alone squeezed his hand!

Kaguyahime was only ten years old; she had been taught to perform all household chores swiftly and very adroitly. A woman's touch turned Nissan's hut into a real home. Suddenly, everything had its place, every corner - peace. Nissan was overjoyed, but he was afraid that he did not know how to show his gratitude to her. However, the little girl noticed even his smallest gesture and clearly made it known to him.

When the Zen monks stopped by at Nissan's, after serving them she would humbly retire to a corner of the room and respond only to Nissan's call. Bit by bit, intrigued by her reticence, the monks would draw her into the conversation. She proved to be very astute and educated.

The following year, the first visible change took place in Nissan's attitude to people, or more precisely, in theirs to him. Samurai Ishi was not the only one to take an interest in little Kaguyahime. Every so often the plantation workers would find various excuses to come to and even enter the hut, all with a view to seeing the little girl. Nissan wondered what it was about her that they found so interesting. He looked upon her as any other child. It was not until he chanced to overhear a conversation between two labourers that he realized they were discussing her wondrous beauty. Accustomed to her as he was, he had not noticed how exceptionally lovely she was.

In the succeeding years, the people's curiosity about her did not wane. On the contrary, more and more travellers stopped by their home, again under various pretexts. Whoever came had to have a strong reason to climb up, because their hut was off the beaten track. Indeed, Nissan had built it in a spot where people would not drop by. From the new passers-by he heard that the whole province knew about Kaguyahime and that the people called her a princess. This news saddened Nissan; even had it not

69

anticipated her future it was enough to disturb their happiness. He was not a selfish man, but the increasingly frequent visits of strangers bothered him. Kaguyahime understood him and let him know that she would comply with whatever he decided. Nissan quickly made up his mind and announced his decision: except for the Zen monks and Bonzon's supervisor, he would receive no one in his home until the girl turned twenty. The law permitted this, and even helped him: all unnecessary arrivals ceased.

They resumed the previous tranquillity of their life. Nissan devoted himself to his daughter and his work, suppressing unpleasant thoughts about the expiry of his decision. Time furtively took its course, only seemingly vanishing from the surface of events.

Nearly ten years passed but not once did Kaguyahime show any desire to change the quiet life the two of them led. Nissan did not know whether she had become aware of her extraordinary beauty, which now he too saw.

The time came for Nissan's ban on visits to their home to expire. He started developing a fear that he would soon lose his daughter. He attributed it to his already advanced age. Even when he did manage to dispel his doubts, he still could not shake off the foreboding of turbulent events to come.

It all began with the appearance of Prince Godo's emissary, who announced the prince's imminent arrival at Nissan's home. Nissan's agitation was assuaged by his daughter's unchanged behaviour. Still, Nissan received the prince's visit uneasily. Enchanted by Kaguyahime's beauty, the prince called her a princess. Kaguyahime did not allow herself to be deterred. In reply to the prince's offer of marriage, she said she would accept (whereupon Nissan went numb with pain), but on one condition: if, with the next full moon, he could tell her how many stars there were in the sky. Prince Godo was surprised, but he promised to try.

Several weeks later, the emissary came to announce that the

prince had not succeeded because the nights were always too short for him to count all the stars. Although the prince had called in his guards to help, he was unable to divide the sky into regular parts so that each one would know which section of stars was his to count.

Kaguyahime merely smiled enigmatically and conveyed her greetings to the prince. Nissan trembled with excitement when he realised that he longer need worry about future suitors. And so it was. For the next few years, Kaguyahime's many admirers lined up in front of Nissan's door, but not one managed to resolve the various assignments the princess gave them. They now called her "the unconquerable." This new attribute of hers prompted the greatest warriors of the realm to try, futilely if persistently, all their finest skills for her. But Kaguyahime remained an unconquerable fortress and gave her hand to no one.

And then the shogun himself, Osson the Younger, announced his arrival. Nissan took to his bed from renewed sorrow. His now advanced years were hard put to master his love for Kaguyahime. He did not want her to see that the possibility of her leaving was the cause of his unhappiness. She assured him that her rejection of suitors was not because of his own devotion to her. This appeased him slightly, but it did not heal him.

The shogun arrived with a large retinue. He set up camp near Nissan's hut and let it be known that he had come with his mind firmly made up. However, Kaguyahime behaved toward him as she did toward all her suitors. The shogun suffered the humiliation painfully, but he took it. He agreed to the condition she set him: he had to name all the one thousand two hundred varieties of bamboo in Japan, China and India. Half of them grew in his own country, but no one other than Obuto Nissan himself knew them all. And he could not ask for Nissan's help. The shogun dispatched men, written requests and orders all over his own and other lands and waited a whole year for the answers, without returning to the capital. Although he tried to govern the country from where he was, he did neglect many state affairs, slowly placing the country, it was felt, in dangerous uncertainty. He appeased his unrequited love by receiving numerous courtesans in his temporary home.

The shogun's final list was not enough for Kaguyahime. Defeated, prior to returning to the capital he asked to see the girl alone. Before her he shed all pride and confessed his love for her, and his decision to marry no other for the rest of his life. Kaguyahime was profoundly moved by such devotion. She decided to tell him the truth which she had hid from everyone else.

"With the next full moon, my guards will come down from the moon for me and take me back, because that is my original home."

The shogun left, but he quickly dispatched two thousand troops, led by the most loyal samurais, to prevent Kaguyahime's departure. To no avail. On the night of the full moon Kaguyahime simply disappeared. Nissan Obuto left his bed no more and the shogun's messenger returned to the capital bearing a letter Kaguyahime had left him.

No witness of the times ever learned the contents of the letter. Before falling to the armies of the rebel rulers, the shogun, Osson the Younger, ordered that the letter be burned with full honours at the top of the highest mountain in the country. And so it was done. Even after the unsuccessful defence of the capital, smoke from the letter continued to rise out of the mouth of the mountain known by the name of Fuji, and also called the Immortal Mountain.

II.

A troubled night loomed over Kagoshima province. It was all in layers, like a cake: one row of silence, another of torrid winds from the open sea. When the winds blew, it was as though one's body had two halves to it: one felt cold from the thighs down, but from there up the body was mostly drenched in sweat squeezed out of it by the wind and then immediately blown dry.

Old Osson felt like a shrivelled fruit: he had dried up from expectation. He thought if he stood on the porch it would quell his nerves, but all it did was create confusion in his organism through which all the seasons of the year alternated at tremendous speed.

Several rooms away, his wife, the princess Konosakya, was bringing into the world his fourth child. He was waiting for an heir. His powers in testing his masculinity were already on the decline. He *had to have a son. For his daughters he had already chosen future husbands who were under obligation to secure him, by virtue of their firm positions in the state, an even greater influence on the shogun. The shogun himself knew the extent to which fear of Osson governed these and all other nobles. Evil was Osson's form of justice.

His personal servant Meno, the epitome of fidelity to his master's every desire, crept up behind him and, his face twisted in conspiracy, said: "Master, the doctor has taken the female bamboo." He left as silently as he had come in.

Osson jumped up with joy: the female bamboo knife was used to cut the umbilical cord of a male infant! Finally all his plans would start bearing fruit. He left his enjoyment of the future for later and quickly returned to his throne room. No one could know that he had already been informed of the sex of the bamboo tree.

Soon the princess's servant brought him the infant. Osson did not have to feign joy. The doctor told him that the child was completely healthy, as was the mother. When everybody had withdrawn, Osson and the doctor went into the garden to plant the bamboo knife, in keeping with custom. The doctor let it drop freely from his hand to the ground. But as it fell, the knife turned upside down and pierced the ground with its handle end. The doctor went pale, and Osson turned red with fury. It was a bad omen for the newborn infant and for the entire family. Osson reacted with lightning speed; he led the doctor into the other courtyard, summoned the guards and ordered them to cut him down immediately. The swords flashed. The doctor's life vanished in the dark.

Meno, following orders, fenced in the planted bamboo, so that no eyes would see it again. He dared not give the slightest sign that he knew what was at stake, let alone that he was and remained the only witness to the doctor's fatal mistake. This would be reason enough for him to part with this life. He, if anyone, knew his master well.

Although he had covered up the trace of the ill omen, Osson was not at peace. He had waited for a male child too long for him to now coldly accept a sign that was not in his favour. He wanted his son to uphold the family's fame for strong masters, and secretly he imagined one of his family becoming the supreme chief. Through his son he wanted to exploit the shogun's favour. It was thanks to Osson's clan that the ruler was quite secure on his throne. Namely, the people of Kagoshima province had complained for years about the brutal rule of Osson and his deputies; about the excessive taxes, harsh fines, torture of prisoners and murder of transgressors, in short, about his unbridled autocracy. However, the shogun neither could nor wanted to take steps against him. Ever-fearful of being overthrown by the other daimyos, on Osson he could count at all times. This, others knew as well. Osson was not loyal to the shogun for romantic reasons, but because of his own strict military upbringing which had taught him, for a lifetime, that one serves the shogun without question. He retained this old trait of the hagakura code which, however antiquated it may have seemed, created numerous concessions and benefits for him. Osson was the only daimyo who still honoured some of the ancient samurai rules so strictly. And that meant he was the only one to be privileged in certain situations. His harsh conduct had the tacit blessing of the shogun. As long as Osson enjoyed the shogun's favour, he could rule as he liked, thus deterring the other daimyos from setting their sights on the palace. With iron discipline he created the strongest army in the state and used it to keep the others in line. They all depended on one another. And so the circle of unchanged events was kept forever closed.

But now Osson's satisfaction had been disturbed by the "up-ended" bamboo and its ominous portent. He was afraid he would never be able to fulfil his dream: to make his son more brutal a ruler than he himself, and thereby even more dangerous and closer to the shogun.

*   *   *

Restlessness virtually swaggered into Osson's days, and especially nights. When everyone serenely surrendered to their dreams, he would look in on his boy, inspecting him from all sides to see whether there was any change. Mistrustful, he changed several doctors in less than a month. Each one assured him that the child was perfectly healthy, which he himself could see. But all this was not enough for him. He decided to enter into collusion with fate. He knew he was thus risking the punishment of secret knowledge, which tests man's strength and disturbs future events. But the uncertainty was stronger than the fear. When it completely overpowered him, he headed for the Kanaka hills, disguised as a servant, taking only Meno with him.

They found the prophetess in the thickest mist on their third day of roaming the almost impenetrable woods of Kanaka. She was sitting in the hollow of a large trunk, shrouded in web-like veils, cackling at something they neither knew nor found funny. For the first time Osson felt abandoned. As though he were stark naked, bereft of his ever-present self-confidence.

When she spoke, the old woman seemed to let only half the uttered words through the hole of her toothless mouth. Her speech was more like hissing.

"You must be wondering why I'm laughing? Well, so would you if could see yourself the way I do. Why didn't that famous Osson, the ruler, come himself, instead of sending you?"

Osson understood the rebuke, but, however much he tried, he failed to recover his lost imperiousness.

"He's nowhere to be seen, old woman. A bad omen is gnawing away at him."

"You're ridiculous, master. But I've become used to your sort. Indeed, you're the only kind of apparition I ever get to see. I have yet to be visited by somebody happy and composed. Somebody who wants to hear bad news. Everybody comes out of fear or in fear and everybody would like to hear of their fine dreams being fulfilled. But there is none of that."

"Are there no exceptions?"

"None. Maybe you'll be the first!"

Did she want to help him or was she just toying with him? Or was she enjoying his helplessness?

"Osson, you are a strong ruler, but an evil man. Your son will be one of the two. Whichever you are afraid of more you should encourage. Your son will be close to the shogun. He will even be the cause of his downfall. Now go!"

Meno, trembling with fear as he crouched in the bushes off to the side, upon hearing these words rushed with the horses to his master and with excessive solicitude hurried him away. Osson mounted his horse thinking about the old woman's words. He saw nothing bad in them, and, the farther they went, the better he felt. The servant observed him out of the corner of his eye, trying to detect any change on his face, which would be the only sure evidence of all that he himself had heard but not understood. When the master at one moment shouted sharply at the horse, whacked it and then galloped through the glade, Meno yelled out happily and raced after him. That was a sign that his ruler had regained his self-confidence.

As the little heir grew, so Osson spent more and more time with him. Sifting through the prophetess's words in his mind for the umpteenth time, having long since decided what he was most afraid of, Osson took advantage of every opportunity to instil in his son the seed of inviolable evil. For him the measure of any act's validity depended on the amount and subtlety of evil. He wanted to divest his son of dilemmas in choosing ways to resolve problems. Strength, in his view, came exclusively from the dark side of one's character. He did not acknowledge the possibility of governing people and situations out of an impulse of goodness. This was man's weakness, not character trait. Combined with power, it could not gain respect.

The first step was to separate the boy from the other children. He had to be persuaded that he was different. Osson had to teach him everything, so that the boy would know the most and know the best. Keenly receptive, the child was quick to learn. Yielding to trust, he accepted his father's choice of solutions. He was still unable to place one choice above others by himself. The entire secret of upbringing, according to Osson, lay in lengthy preparations for ensuring that unwanted dilemmas did not arise, and this, in most cases, could be accomplished by extensive, serious ground work. The entire concerted approach to the struggle against an as yet non- existent problem was aimed at creating an ideal, exceptionally intuitive and practical ruler with his feet on the ground. He used the example of his own success which made everybody think of him as a man with the gift of simplifying even the biggest problem in an extremely short interval of time. Nobody knew how many presumed situations Osson had resolved before the actual dilemma ever arose. Therein lay the secret of his cruelty, it stemmed from decisions as yet untested in practice but already taken in his mind. It transpired that some details visible to him alone had already been typologically compartmentalised, thereby enabling him to react swiftly. The fairness of the solutions belonged to another world, a world that did not even exist for Osson.

Osson the Younger grew by the day into a handsome, well-built young man. His father was pleased with the results of the physical and mental training he had imposed on his son. He was already slowly testing the boy's ability to make independent decisions of his own. The young man's behaviour, to his father's unconcealed pride, followed the rules of the upbringing he had received.

In the country the balance of forces among the rulers remained unaltered. The only visible change was that Osson and the shogun had grown old. Ever since the shogun had expressed his attachment to Osson's heir, they met regularly. The young man began coming to his ruler even without invitation, and soon he had unlimited access everywhere. The son depicted himself as a modest, mild man, leaving Osson to marvel at his superb acting, and above all at his own personal contribution to this ability of his son's. His goal had almost been achieved. He announced his pending retirement and the proclamation of his son as the ruler of Kagoshima province. The shogun gave his approval and soon the Osson family's young ruler was celebrated as the new hope of the splintered, only seemingly quiet state. But the young man did not get to demonstrate the nuances of his character. The events that followed caught him in a very strange position. Namely, his proclamation as ruler of the province was used by all the daimyos to rebel, not against Osson, but against the shogun. Emboldened by the elder Osson's departure from power, the rulers of the other provinces, hitherto patient, now stormed the capital with their armies.

Hearing of the rebellion, the young man quickly collected an army and, with his father's blessing, set out on a belated defence of the shogun. He was aware of the superiority of so many armies over his own, but the fury that suffused him did not bode well for his opponents. The latter had obviously anticipated this, and at the gates to the capital there was a surprise in store for him. All the daimyos peacefully awaited him there, bearing negotiating banners. A fresh surprise ensued; they offered him the place of shogun! They assured him that he alone in the country was capable of shouldering such a responsibility. He asked for a day to think it over and withdrew his army from the walls.

He sensed a trap, but was unable to pin-point it. However, to reject the offer without a clear reason was senseless. To fight them all, which is what refusal would oblige him to do, brought no certainty. What would his father advise him in a case like this? Well, of course, to outsmart them. And if you are faced with too many unknowns, then at least take time as your own, and it will provide a solution. Here time meant - accepting the offer.

The daimyos, not without fear of the uncertainty of his response, received his acceptance with relief. Indeed, it meant achieving the following goals: to impose on an overly young and inexperienced ruler as many obligations as possible, thereby relieving themselves of these same obligations, and to use his busyness and inexpertise for ruling their own provinces, and him himself, unhindered. By the time he saw through their plans and the deeds already done, it would be too late. Then it would again come time to think up new reasons for overthrowing the shogun.

None of them could foresee everything. Within Osson the Younger, who above all wanted peace in the country, the desire to punish the ruler's assassins won out. For, he had only just assumed office when he learned that they had not spared the old shogun nor allowed him to carry out seppuku. Unworthy of the position, they had killed him, and with him his entire family. And so Osson the Younger acted immediately. He summoned the rulers to an important meeting, and ordered his samurais to cut them all down to the very last one. He appointed his military commanders as the new rulers and dispatched them to the provinces s o that with their new armies they might finish what had been begun.

Overjoyed, Osson came to his son in the palace to praise his wise decisions and cruel deeds. He wondered where that bad omen from his son's birth was. The words of the prophetess had come true! His son had even become a strong ruler. Ah, but yes! According to her words he could not at the same time be an evil man. Osson would be devastated by the very possibility of his son becoming good. For now, the son had demonstrated his determination, and in it there was no goodness. The public trial he staged for the samurai who had tortured the shogun prior to his being cut down, could not be a sign of weakness on the part of the new ruler as much as one of hitherto unusual fairness toward his predecessor. Indeed, it won him many supporters among the people. Osson believed that this too was a well-calculated move on his son's part. Or he simply convinced himself of it.

The father and all those close to him, started trying to persuade the young shogun that the time had come for him to think about his progeny. And so the shogun soon announced that he would take as his wife a certain princess who was not really a princess, by the name of Kaguyahime, the daughter of the woodkeeper, one of his subjects. Her father, whose name was Obuto Nissan, was not really her father. She was said to have come out of the bamboo. The shogun quickly prepared an escort and headed toward his fate. He was away courting for a whole year. . .

III.

On the second day of his reign, Osson the Younger was awoken by a commotion in the palace courtyard. Meno, until recently his father's servant, rushed into his chamber, visibly upset and frightened.

"Master, forgive me for disturbing you, but Seko, the late shogun's personal samurai, has come to the palace. He wants to confess to you before he commits seppuku at daybreak and joins his master."

Osson nodded and the guard led the man in.

"What is tormenting you so badly that you had to come now?"

"Master, I'm ashamed to confess. I have been hiding since the day they murdered our shogun. Because of my helplessness in the face of what I saw and because of my cowardice, at dawn I shall leave this body. I want you to receive this testimony in place of my fear," and he offered the shogun a letter, rolled up, tied and sealed.

"But please do not open it until after my death. I wanted to look you in the eyes and be sure that you received it. I would not offend you with my presence were the letter not important. May others serve you better than they did our late ruler. Forgive me."

Bowing, Seko departed.

In the morning Meno informed the young Osson that the samurai had carried out his pledge.

The letter contained some very unpleasant facts about the last hours of the shogun's life, and it was signed with the name of the samurai Seko. At first Osson the Younger was appalled, but then he was seized by raging fury. He summoned Meno and ordered him to have the palace guard personally bring him the samurai Senzaki, who was in prison on suspicion of conspiracy in the murder of the old shogun and his family.

He spoke briefly with Senzaki, and then issued orders to his commanders that not a single daimyo was to come out alive from the meeting he would arrange that day with all the rebel rulers, but would not attend himself. By day's end, the capital was rife with the terrible story of how all the former shogun's chief assistants had been cut down.

The next day Osson announced the decision to put the samurai Senzaki on trial.

When the trial opened a few days later, everyone present was surprised by the arrival of Osson, who declared he would attend the entire trial.

First the charges against Senzaki were read out, accusing him of shamelessly torturing the ruler, thereby causing his death. Those present were shocked. Unwritten laws did not allow for the possibility of disgracing a shogun.

Samurai Seko's letter described the method used to torture the shogun by previously unknown means. They had laid out the shogun on a firmly rooted bench, tying him to it face-down. The bench had two hollowed out holes in it: one, roundish, for the stomach, and the other, somewhat narrower, at eye-level, so that the shogun could see the surface beneath him. Directly underneath the opening for the stomach the soldiers planted a bamboo shoot, and then withdrew. Senzaki remained close by to control the direction in which the plant grew. The fast-growing ma-dake bamboo, the most widespread of its kind in Japan, rushed voraciously toward its goal. It took approximately twelve hours for it to cover the sixty-centimetre height of the bench. A careful observer, such as Senzuki and the hidden Seko, could see how the plant was advancing. When the shogun began to show signs of pain, Senzaki sent the guard for the daimyos. For almost two hours the sharp tip of the shoot dug itself a passage through the shogun's body. The shogun was alive until the bamboo burst through his back. With one last surge of strength, he shortened his suffering by banging his head against the bench. That was the end.

Senzaki did not confess to the deed of which he stood accused. He kept saying that the shogun had been killed without torture, that he himself had carried out the death sentence, on orders from the daimyos. Neither truth could be established: the shogun's body had not been found.

The court condemned Senzaki to death.

IV.

My beloved,

Only now that I travel other firmaments different from yours on whose surface you remained sad and burning, can I confess how much of my love I left you. You should feel it like the armful of kindling you would carry into your house: it's there, but it isn't heavy. And how did you use that armful? You didn't put all of it into the stove and light it, but rather just a twig to start up the coal. And when did you use it? When you were cold. Did it help you resolve any of life's mysteries? No, but it did enable you to start quietly thinking about them. Did it warm you up just a little? Yes, that it certainly did.

Once you had burned up the entire armful, were ashes all that was left or did you still feel in your blood the warmth of the one-time fire?

I spent ten years in plants, knowing you existed. Another ten years with my foster father, your subject, who had the most beautiful occupation in the world. I plunged that wonderful woodkeeper of yours into unhappiness just to lay eyes on you. I know I also made him happy. No one knows, nor should know, that I existed solely because of our two encounters, and the one and only year that I was near you.

Far away from your country lives an animal people call the king of all animals. It is indeed the strongest, the fastest, the nimblest, wise and terrifying. All people and all animals know that it is the king, except for the animal itself. It is as though it can do almost anything, as though there are no obstacles before it. And when it hides from man, it does so not out of fear but because it is shrewd and clever.

I know the fate of the old shogun and his assassins. The evil-doers should be punished, but not the ma-dake. Bamboo has a soul, but you don't know that. It would never pass through a man's body. It would touch it and look for another way around it. Plant one at home and let it have an obstacle made of whatever you like above it. You'll see that it won't even try to go through it, but like a vine will seek space, not objects, for its life. People grow and live through other people, positions, objects instead of through space

82

which is their spiritual abode. There are no obstacles in it because here man fights himself, his willpower, his strength. Here matter does not exist.

That's why one can love somebody all one's life, if one decides to: again it is a battle with, but not against oneself.

Have you ever asked yourself what it means to be successful, especially a successful ruler? Is ruling perhaps not the worst form of showing personal dissatisfaction, of failure to come to terms with oneself and one's views. The strongest (and the cruellest) rulers are the unhappiest people in the world. They try to transfer their undefined restlessness to the struggle for power. Obuto Nissan once conveyed to me his knowledge of this, compressing it into two sentences:

1) If you haven't learned to rule yourself, you will probably learn to do so by ruling others, although one forgets that with time ruling others eradicates the need for ruling (over) oneself.

2) If you haven't learned to rule yourself, you'll probably make up for it by ruling (over) others.

The truth of an unfulfilled life is admitted only in and not before one's deathbed. For those who even then fail to understand this, the last thing they feel before dark death is a strange bitterness in their mouth. They don't know that this bitterness is - unhappiness.

And happiness? Happiness has always been attained by the least expected means:a hand on an expectant mother's stomach, an evenly hollowed ladle dipped into the soup dish, a word that is yours but uttered by another, a look at the scabby sky out of which peers the non-existent point of the Shooting Star. . . Few are wise enough not to even try to bring to the surface what they consider important in their everyday lives. Because ordinary things are as big and important as we ourselves consider them to be, and need not be placed above others. All small things are equally beautiful, they merely need to be tied into a silk knotless skein and rolled.

From where I am looking at you, everything appears quite different. Battles are like senselessly chasing the wind. Those who consider themselves to be big are equally small and big like everyone else. When Obuto inspected the groves, he marvelled not *at the imagined forms and traits of the bamboo but at what he saw on them and what he knew about them. Only what he saw and knew, and others didn't, separated him from them. He was searching for something that was here around him, something small, simple and ordinary, but extant and not outside the life he was leading.*

If a person does not find himself in his environment, then he would do better not to exist at all. The environment is always near, sometimes too near for us to recognize it.

Kaguyahime

V.

"Have I broken with my previous life?" I wondered, standing before the closed doors of the Dabou-ji Monastery. "Am I certain that the past will be the past?" Of course I wasn't certain. That's what I wished, but I believed I would fulfil my desire for oblivion more easily if I told myself that there was no past. But how, when there was? I sought a way that would not deny the existence of what had already been, but that would reconcile the remains of the past with the desire to attain a goal unknown to me. I searched for something that was awaiting me. To choose from the known was no solution. I had to let new knowledge cleanse me of the rot that was spreading like a cobweb across my soul.

Vestiges are the worst enemy. One fights pain without thinking, without a plan, because nature tells one to resist. Then it is not a solution that is sought, but a defence, a way out of the pain. When victory is incomplete, the vestiges of the wound become worse than the wound itself. One doesn't know what to do with them, one cannot go against them because to get the better of them means to have a known, visible, sure solution. That, in turn, calls for a strong, cold-blooded fighter who knows what to do with victory. A man exhausted by boulders has no strength left to collect pebbles and becomes more vulnerable than he was when the trumpets first sounded the charge.

Such was I, standing in front of the large wooden doors of

Dabou-ji.

They were opened by somebody I didn't see. Perhaps they had opened by themselves. In front of me was a pebbled path lined on either side by young bamboo stalks which served as guides to the porch of one of the buildings. I stopped at the broad step on which there was a bench. Above it stood a sparkling clean porch of dark, even boards. I doffed my hat, untied my belt, removed the bundle from my back and put everything down in front of me. I struck the little hammer against the gong on its stand to announce my presence, took out the piece of paper with my application on it and then, half-sitting on the bench, stooping over, I leaned my forehead against my hands which rested on the bundle. I waited in that position for someone to appear. After more than two hours, not daring to move, I heard steps approaching. Not raising my head I saw the hand that picked up my application. From a kneeling position, the voice asked me:

"Who are you?"

"My name is Ts'ao and I would like to become an unsui here."

"What roshi did you study under before?"

"I have had no other teacher than my own will."

"Wait a minute," he said and left.

I remained in that same position for a few more hours until another monastery official appeared.

"There is no more room in this monastery for disciples and we cannot admit you."

I was persistent. I moved not a finger. I knew they were testing my endurance and willpower and that they were watching me. The pain in my back, knees and fingers increased. At nightfall the first official reappeared.

"The discipline here is strict. You would do better to go someplace else."

For me, a beginner, there could be no other place. If I gave up now, everybody would quickly hear of it and no monastery would take me. Giving up could depend only on my (non-)endurance. The pain became unbearable. But I remained riveted to my hands and the ground beneath me. Niwazume implied, apart from immobility, total silence. I did not respond to any of the repulsive, insulting statements addressed to me. Had I uttered but a word, I would have been thrown out of the courtyard immediately and never allowed to pass through the shoji again.

Evening fell. I no longer felt my body. I thought I would collapse any minute. Then one of the hosts came up and left in front of me a dish of rice. Slowly, so that they would not distinguish the pain and fear from the faintness, I raised myself into a sitting position and ate my dinner. I then immediately resumed my previous position. This time I did not have long to wait. I was told that I could spend the night in the tankaryo, but that I had to leave the monastery in the morning. The thin reed mat I was given seemed so comfortable, that I fell asleep the moment I lay down on it. I had neither dreams nor nightmares. I just slept and when I awoke a moment later it was morning. I immediately folded the futon and returned to my place of the day before and the position of obeisance, disregarding yesterday's order to leave the garden. Somewhat used to the pain in my body now, I found it easier to bear the waiting until the next test. At noon, I was given, along with a few new insults, the same meal as the previous day. Toward day's end, all the pain vanished, numbed by swellings on my hands and legs. I felt as though my face had swelled up. The monastery official appeared once again.

"Since you seem to have a sincere desire to enter, we shall put you in the tankaryo. But don't think that everything will now be all right and that your efforts will be diminished. We may throw you out at any minute."

I spent the next four days closed up in the room. I saw only the hand that brought a full and removed an empty dish of food. To be in the tankaryo meant that I had received temporary permission to be in this confined space. The real tribulations were yet to come. I had to spend the whole time in a sitting position, only slightly more comfortable than the one before, and concentrate on myself and my innerness. I could interupt the practice of zazen only when I was brought food. I was free to sleep a few hours at night, but I used almost all of them for zazen. The aggravating circumstance of my never having had a teacher but just self-taught wise men who passed on to me their own personal experience, did not allow me the possibility of choice: I had to show to the full my desire to stay. The other problem was my laic knowledge of the practice of zazen: I did not know what it was supposed to provoke inside me, what it was supposed to change and achieve. The stories told by others were not enough. So I tried to be as calm as I could, without oppressive thoughts. So much time lay ahead of me that, considering my knowledge so far, I had to fill it up with something. During the first two days various thoughts entered my head, which rather upset me. Fortunately, I would always remind myself in time where I was and why. Then, for a while, I found a solution by repeating all the acts and movements I had performed in front of the monastery and in its garden. Upon reconsideration, it was I who opened the monastery doors. I just touched them gently and they revealed the luxuriant surroundings. Namely, Dabou-ji stood atop Mount Shito, actually on the last plateau before the peak itself. When the great doors opened, one looked out onto the vegetation and paths above the temple which seemed to have grown out of the rooftops of the monastery buildings. The silence was almost absolute. The morning birds had already announced themselves and were now busy with their daily chores. One could only hear the soft gurgling of the stream that rushed down the mountain slope to the plateau, where it reduced its haste and, like a vain, splendidly colourful bird, paraded its beauty, and then, after saying: "Now you've seen me as I can be," hurried mightily on, as though somewhere down below it had an important meeting for which it was already very late.

Walking past the guard of bamboo toward the zendo porch just when these steadfast sentries were looking the other way, I saw in front of the main entrance to the zazen hall a statue of the temple's royal guard in a pose of anticipated danger with a terrifying half-open mouth and eyes staring at the newcomer. The zendo window next to it had a wooden frame shaped like the lick of a flame. Was all this meant to scare away undesirables or discourage those uncertain of their wish to stay here?

On the porch by the spot where I had removed the bundle from my back, behind the big gong that hung together with the wooden hammer on its own stand, was a canvas with large calligraphic inscriptions that were beautiful in shape but unknown to me. Then I thought how anything unknown looked terrifying to me. I was right. Ignorance breeds fear.

Acceptance of this truth helped me to resume my awkward zazen more calmly and more certain of the outcome. I stopped asking myself what I was really doing here, what I wanted, etc.

Toward the end of the fourth day I was informed of the decision that I could join the other unsuis at the Dabou-ji monastery.

Following instructions, I again found myself by the porch. One of the disciples brought me a pail of water. I removed my straw sandals and tabi. I had to wash my feet thoroughly so as not accidentally to dirty the tatami in any of the rooms. As I was pouring water on my feet, I received a heavy blow on the back. Standing over me was one of the officials with a rod in his hand.

"Save every drop of water!"

I tied together the socks and sandals in silence and slipped on the wooden sandals I had been given for use outside the room. I stood up and looked around. Everything around me exuded serenity. I wondered whether I would find it within myself.

VI.

Senzaki was exempted from working in the stone quarry after he was condemned to death. His comfort was seen to. So as to make the punishment all the greater, he was moved from the common cells to a solitary one. Although he found it hard being alone he thought he would find idleness even harder to endure if he were surrounded by criminals. While still awaiting trial, he had heard from them stories about people who seemed to have stepped straight out of a book on incredible phenomena. Worst of all, all these murderers and thieves had accepted him as one of their own. He was an equal among them, and even enjoyed a position of respect as an extremely courageous person who had dared to raise a hand against the shogun himself. No dissuasion, in an attempt to explain that he was not guilty, was of any help. For them he was an admirable if rather modest prisoner. He realized then that there can be two truths and that the one need not rule out the other; on the contrary. It was as though his whole life were laid out on the palm of his now closing hand. In the better case, he would be blown away like a sweet little bug which, dazed by the heat, had stopped to rest on a monster who was momentarily in a good humour.

Senzaki had carried out the commands of his master not because the shogun was irreproachably fair but because he had never asked himself whether these were the only proper orders that could be given. Now he wondered whether he had not been the executor of hundreds of assignments like this. To this extent he understood the possibility of error.

He asked the guard to inform the prison commander Ishimatsu that he wished to speak to him alone. Surprisingly enough, the commander received him immediately. Senzaki was somewhat afraid of Ishimatsu's reaction to what he wanted to say, because he knew the man personally. Their last meeting had not been very propitious for the prison warden. On orders from the shogun, Senzaki had checked how the state laws were being implemented in the prison. As far as Senzaki knew, his visit was to be followed by Ishimatsu's arrest for embezzlement and reports of inhumane treatment of the prisoners. The latter charge was not so important: such conduct was a routine occurrence in state prisons. But by sacrificing Ishimatsu, the shogun wanted to win fresh support from the people and the individual daimyos.

"You see, Senzaki, how fickle luck is. Had you not done me a service, I would now be sitting here in front of you or somebody else, thinking up ways to absolve myself of as much guilt as possible. But since our conscientious ruler is dead, I remain in your debt. I cannot do much for you; your life is out of my hands, but I can listen to you if, such as now, you have something to say to me."

Senzaki did his best to refrain from reacting to such a cynical welcome. He had to control his emotions and embark on his plan calmly, as though he had not heard the tasteless comparison. This time even swords would not alleviate the hatred that stood between them as deeply as an ocean.

"Ishimatsu, I have not come to ask for anything. I have come to make a proposal."

"Oho, so there is still some pride left in you. I'm afraid you are in no position to set terms."

"True. That is why I shall just talk, and you be patient enough to hear me out. If you're willing, that is."

Ishimatsu did not reply and Senzaki said what was on his mind in a single breath.

"You know about the rhinoceros horn trade. If you want to get rich without too much effort, I can help you. I know the location of the secret storage place of the Assam bamboo from which the horns are made. There's so much that all your guards together wouldn't be able to transport it by cart. In return, I ask you to let me go. I wouldn't be much use to you dead."

Ishimatsu's eyes lit up. Conscious of his own greed, he lowered his eyes and asked as though thoughtfully: "What guarantee do I have that you are telling the truth?"

"This. You shall send your man to a place nearby to take just a few of the horns, and when you are convinced of the truth of what I am saying, we can talk again. But please do it quickly. I do not have many days left. Neither have you."

"What do you mean - neither have I?"

"Why, I meant that you should already ensure yourself against the dangerous hand of the new shogun. He did away with all the daimyos in short order. Do you really think he will leave somebody like you in a position like this? Even if you admitted to him that you stole from the former shogun, it wouldn't really help you to ingratiate yourself with him. Then you'd see the full force of his justice. And I don't think it's very smart to wait and see how long you'll be warden."

Ishimatsu did not reply. Having told him how to find samples of the horn, Senzaki returned to his cell.

The warden was a man of quick action. The very next morning the guards came for Senzaki.

"You spoke the truth. The bamboos are quality, the

workmanship is excellent. Nobody has discovered the forgery. I agree to further negotiations. I'm listening."

Senzaki breathed a quick, deep sigh of relief, as much as the situation allowed. He had to remain on even ground. Concealing his joy, Senzaki proceeded to reveal to him the rest of the plan.

"The storage place is a night's walk and sail away, toward the Chinese coast. Have some of your men go with me, and you too if you like. Your part of the job is to make my escape look convincing. Once you're sure that the treasure I'm offering you really does exist, I promise nobody will ever see me in this country again. I'll stay in China forever. You make certain that you are not held responsible for my escape. Better that you yourself decide on whether to stay in this post or not, than have somebody else do it for you."

"All right. I'll see to it that nobody notices your absence for three days. Just in case your story proves false. In that event, we put you back in chains. As for my own plans, don't you worry. I know what I'm doing."

Senzaki had to admit to himself that his rival really did know what he was doing.

"Tonight your food will be brought by a guard who is already preparing to become a minion of the new shogun's. You will have a weapon with you. You will kill him. If you don't, the agreement is off. His corpse will be found within the said three days. The rest is my job. We have finished."

Senzaki knew that he must not ask himself whether or not to carry out this perfidious murder. When he had decided to negotiate with Ishimatsu, he had known that it meant agreeing to everything. And so the dilemma merely flashed before him and quickly vanished.

Slipping into the role of blind executor of the commander's plan, Senzaki carried out his part of the agreement in the prison itself. Outside were Ishimatsu's men. Riding their horses at a gallop, they reached the coast where Ishimatsu's crew, captain and flagless ship were ready waiting for them. They sailed off into the nocturnal sea. Dawn found them hidden in one of the coves of Yentai Bay. Senzaki showed them the cave full of Assam bamboo horns. While Ishimatsu and his retinue gazed in wonder at their future cargo, Senzaki slipped through a secret passage out to the other side of the mountain and disappeared into the woods of Tsingtao Province. He was prudent enough to escape in time from the eyes bloodshot with greed as they gazed upon a treasure that does not like witnesses.

VII.
I made my first serious mistake while waiting for something to happen. Since I had repeatedly waited in vain for the answer to questions posed to my cohabitants, I had to turn to and within myself to find the answers. At the monastery virtually everything that was done from dawn till dusk, and sometimes even into the night, fell within a code of conduct that basically did not permit conversation, so that contact among the disciples was reduced to the joint performance of their duties, but in total silence. Everybody spoke up together during the recital of the sutra, as one accord but with others' texts. Abbreviated conversations were conducted when in contact with the roshi, but in the solitude of practising koan. For the time being, the teacher did not give us joint lectures. Even after having spent several days here, I did not see him personally. And that was my mistake; I expected a formal meeting with him, and that could happen when I least expected it. Until then my supervisor was Tetsujiro, who was in charge of overseeing everything in the monastery. Not just that: he was the man who solved problems, carried out the solutions and served as the main bridge between all the brethren. He had the title of daishi. He was already very old, but he did not want to be set apart in any job. He did everything that the youngest disciples did. I saw him work the garden, perform the Chinese arts, carry wood and move rocks with equal deftness. For all that physical labour, his hands enchanted me: they were thin, gentle hands with finely sculpted fingers the length of which was quite amazing. When he pressed together his hands while uttering the sutra, I would steal a glance at them imagining how they ended somewhere up by the

ceiling. Something extraordinary radiated from them. They had a strange affect on me: whenever I felt distraught, and was in a position to search for them, a mere glance at those hands sufficed for me to calm down and return to what I had been doing. His face was gently wrinkled, dry, long, with a high brow.

I imagined the roshi, whom I had not yet seen, as a man of exceptional qualities whom I could not picture in entirely ordinary situations. To me he was the epitome of everything I could not yet grasp. As though I liked the idea of such a person existing, I feared ever seeing him because, I thought, it might destroy the magic I had already spun around him.

However, Tetsujiro was in an even less favourable position. His title, apart from the burden of responsibility, also gave him the most menial daily chores which the uninitiated would view with contempt. I still did not know enough about him, but I had infinite confidence in him. When I finally saw him one day, on his knees, his robes gathered between his legs, scrubbing the common latrine, I was stunned. Why, this man combined in him the uncombinable! When he did it, it looked so normal, so unassuming, divested of any thought of pride, rank or age. The peace that emanated from him was his distinguishing mark, but it also marked the possible attainment of space wherein one did not think about it at all, one just worked.

While he explained to me the daily schedule of all the unsuis' activities, with minor changes relating to me, Tetsujiro's face remained completely expressionless as though someone else were speaking the sentences he had probably uttered so many times.

In spring and summer, the day began at three in the morning by rinsing out one's mouth from a ladle of water, washing and reciting the morning sutras. Disciples who so wished, could then speak with the teacher alone. Meanwhile the others would practice zazen until breakfast. Then came zazen again and the daily cleaning of the rooms, clothes and articles. On set days, the roshi gave joint lectures for all the disciples from seven in the morning. These lessons were conducted only a few months in the year. On the days appointed for begging (every third day after the second day of the month), they went outside the monastery to the nearby villages. Lunch was served at ten on lecture days, and at eleven if going begging. After lunch the priests could practice zazen. Manual labour started at one in the afternoon. Before dinner, served at three-thirty or four, the evening sutras were recited. At twilight, it was again time for zazen. After that, the roshi was available to anyone who wished to visit him in his room. The day formally ended at eight o'clock in winter and nine o'clock in summer. The night was envisaged for sleeping, but the disciples could practice zazen then too, although outside the room, on the porch.

Of all the above, I was actually able to do little together with the other, more experienced disciples. I did not visit the roshi, I did not go begging, I practised zazen imperfectly. The roshi was still not giving lectures, so I did not even know what they were like. I filled the entire time planned for these exercises by working in the kitchen, in the garden, by washing the rooms, in short by helping out with all the chores that actually had nothing to do with what I was preparing for. At least so I thought. I was equal to others on those dates in the month that had the numbers four and nine in them, when we bathed and shaved our heads.

In both summer and winter, during the period of ango, the disciples had especially difficult training from the first to the seventh, the eleventh to the seventeenth and the twenty-first to the twenty-seventh day of every month. The hardest exercises similar to these were from the first to the morning of the eighth of December, in observance of the enlightenment of Sakyamuni. These days were filled exclusively with the practice of zazen and talks with the roshi, which lasted day and night. The very name of the exercise, rohatsu dai seshin, implied intense concentration of the mind.

Even after several months at Dabou-ji, these exercises remained beyond my reach. I performed my duties, but there was no joy in my heart. Separated from the others, I suffered and slowly lapsed into apathy. The only bright light in the monotony of the day was daishi Tetsujiro whose frail figure often stood by my side as though sometimes he were doing my chores with me or in my stead. His task was to see that everybody performed his duties, but it was as though this was not his only purpose in being near me. However, I was unable to uncover his hidden reasons, if there were any.

Initially, the pledge of almost total silence among the disciples, and the busy daily schedule that made it impossible for us to talk to one another more than we did, suited me perfectly. Everything was very new and unfamiliar to my inner confusion and disconcertion, and in my personal disquiet, which was still not in touch with the essence of my space, I found reasons for the excessive oscillation between harmony and disharmony with the circumstances. I spent my few free moments in solitude, walking the paths of the monastery garden whose vegetation instilled confidence and calmed the soul. But as time passed, and I remained of little use to myself, I found less and less consolation in these walks. The garden was beautiful, but the thought that they would not even let me maintain it on my own, destroyed my last line of support. I thought: "How ironic; anyone watching me tread these paths would think I had reached the heights of absolute serenity and harmony." Yet I was walking out of pure habit and the dependence created by time.

"I see you have a strong desire to do kinhin, but you started it sooner than you should!"

The voice was deep and unfamiliar. I turned around and froze. From the clothes he wore, I recognized the teacher. I was unable to utter a word, but he certainly was not. I did not even have time to take in his face, before he went on.

"Zazen in walking is practised by experienced disciples. However, since you are already trying it, do it properly. You are combining two ways of kinhin, but you should follow just one. You walk softly like a Soto monk, but quickly the way our Rinzai school would teach you. Although, if you achieve what you wish, it's all the same to me. I'd even let you fly. When you decide which is better, come to me. Let it be tomorrow morning."

As he spoke he turned around and with a quick step disappeared. I only had time to sigh: "Roshi!"

VIII.

Somebody had been present when Senzaki murdered the prison guard. Disguised as a guard, he waited for Senzaki to make his next move. Nobody could have connected the sudden release of the samurai Ishi, the supervisor of daimyo Bonzon's bamboo groves, with Meno's witnessing of this murder. Meno would have given more than one paltry life for such information.

He followed Ishimatsu's group until they embarked on the ship and he awaited their return at the same spot where he had seen them off, but this time surrounded by a hundred soldiers. The troops were aboard the ship as soon as it laid anchor. When he had checked the cargo, Meno ordered that only their thieving heads be kept for the shogun. Meno did not even ask Ishimatsu about Senzaki. As soon as he saw that Senzaki was not among them, he knew what the commander had done. He merely called out to him: "Now you'll be keeping him company!" Those were the last words Ishimatsu heard. Then Meno dismissed the escort, retaining just a few people personally disposed to him, with whom he took the boat away in a direction known to them alone.

Meno reported on his secret assignment to the shogun and the military commanders. He brought for inspection the remains of the traitors, with the information that Senzaki had been killed by the prison warden. No mention was made of the cargo. He reported that the boat had sunk.

"You have performed your assignment well. Tomorrow you will announce that the death sentence has been carried out against the shogun's torturer. You shall be rewarded."

Meno had already rewarded himself amply with the rich cargo. He had been patiently waiting for an opportunity like this for years, certain that sooner or later it would come. He had spent his entire life in the shadow of Osson the Elder, subordinating his entire personality to blind obedience which, out of habit, he had never once questioned. The only way to give one's life completely to someone else lies in a small but, deeply, deeply hidden secret, which may even seem unimportant, but which is never revealed to anyone. It is the straw for all the trepidation, humiliation, pain, poverty and injustice one dismisses. It is saviour and lover at moments of loneliness, in dreams, when one plunges into the abyss of the seeming stupor of sleep, when we lose touch with ourselves, let alone with others. It is kissed as no other shall ever be because it belongs to our corporality, to ours alone. It is not just in the soul; were it, it would evaporate like an evening cup of sake under the lining of the cerebrum. It is a queen enthroned for as many years as we have left.

Meno put up with it because he knew that, even if he looked for one himself, he would never find a better teacher for keeping and carrying out a secret, for ruthlessness and success, than his own lord Osson. As soon as he sensed what his ruler was aiming at, he would already be gloating over the advantages the barely germinating idea would bring, because Osson unerringly succeeded. And when he realized that the father was planning a place for the son close to the shogun's throne, he was not frightened by the arrogant greed but rather gave generous, unquestioning help to his master, fulfilling his every, others would say, whim. He alone knew that Osson the Elder was a whimless man. Everything, even the most seemingly crazy detail, was part of a well-devised plan. Through his unassuming presence, Meno simply fought to learn what the plan was. Then he would become his master's icy, unfeeling extended arm which shrank at nothing in carrying out orders. Osson had infinite trust in him, although he could never quite explain it to himself. When he would tell Meno his assignment, he never recommended the method because he knew that the servant would invent it even if it seemed not to exist. Such trust between master and servant created a relationship in which love never once appeared as the basis for an act. There was some kind of bond, known to them alone, that even those with a greater experience of life could not recognize. Who would have guessed that the two men's courage and boldness was the result of mutual support?

When Osson the Younger assumed power, Meno came to understand fully the limitless might of his ruler, Osson the Elder, for whom this seemed to be the ultimate objective of all the battles he had won, and so he informed Meno that he could now leave this world. That same evening the father died, retaining only his servant by his pillow. He pledged him to continue serving his son.

"Serve him unless he becomes good. If that were to happen I would renounce him. If he relents in evil, there will be no time for anyone to rebuke him. He will disappear as if he had never existed."

Meno wondered whether Osson the Elder was not also a prophet, without knowing it.

INTERWORD

POSSESSING ABANDONED WORKS

Should the *Foreword* be perceived as an integral whole placed in front of what it precedes in order to explain something too deeply hidden in the pages that follow? Should the *Afterword*, because it comes after the last read sentence of what it succeeds, define or confine the reader's planned interpretation? Or do the one and the other serve to highlight visible, but to the writer important, details? Or are both there for the positive mystification of what is at hand and for expanding the possibilities of multifaceted reading? And what about the *Interword*?

THE FORTUITY OF THE POSSIBLE

If I ever did have a dilemma of the sort articulated in the opening rhetorical questions, it was resolved (as so often happens) by chance [1]. There was a seemingly inconsequential news item that to me meant a great deal. Firstly, that a close relative of one of the heroes of this book had been discovered, and that the "theory"

I so strongly advocate, despite the dearth of facts, and that I had developed before reading this short item, was firmly rooted in the learning of others as well. Secondly, for the umpteenth time I rejoiced at the proof of a never-ending truth: that everything is open, everything is (still) possible... But it all *was possible* as well.

However, this is not to explain, justify or advocate the writer's so-called absolute freedom of imagination, a game without limits, or the loose connection of the unconnectable. This is the *possibility* of all that is permissible within the strictly conceived theme. And, therefore, it includes the possibility of raising questions.

TIME ENCLOSED IN A BOX

Time is the most challenging but also the most dangerous of phenomena, one we sometimes try to enslave with our intentions. That's in the West. In the Far East time is something else. It exists, with many variations, as a moment which the past, present and future identify with the momentary. And vice versa [2]. The Chinese "preferred to see in time an integral whole composed of eras, seasons and epochs." [3] Just how far this notion of time went is eloquently shown by the importance attached in various rituals to having the emperor and his entourage dressed in accordance with the seasons. Once summer formally began, the wearing of green robes which corresponded with the trees, an element of spring, would have meant causing inconceivable offence to the Sky and Earth; all formal robes, banners and cult objects had to be red because this was the colour of *fire*, an element of summer [4]. However, I cannot resist giving an even more concrete illustration of how the Chinese associate faith with "the colour of time," in connection with the aforementioned, albeit "superfluous", element of metal among Greek (i.e. European) philosophers. In about the year 543, Qiwu Huaiwen, the great Daoist swordsmith and metallurgist (probably the inventor of the technique for obtaining steel), advised the emperor Gao Zu of the Eastern Wei dynasty to change the colour of his dynasty's banners from red to yellow (in keeping with the theory of the five elements) if he wanted to defeat the Western Wei dynasty (!).

AUTHENTICITY

The characters are, by definition, as authentic as is necessary for them to be convincing. They (or their relationships) conceal many other characters. These are people whose names (i.e. works) have *outgrown* the impressions left by reading what they signed, and so they have entered my list of the book's (in)visible heroes. Omitting the names of those from my (and our) closest circle, names that would mean nothing to anyone, I shall mention just a few familiar to most people: Christopher Columbus, Marguerite Yourcenar, R.M. Pirsig, Joseph Needham, Umberto Eco, Yukio Mishima, Marco Polo, Julio Cortazar, Henry Lincoln, Vojtech Zamarovsky and many others. They have collaborated on this book. Its actual creators, the authors (of Part One or Part Two) are also many: Sung Shan, Ernest Wood, Obuto Nissan, T. O. Ling, Christmas Humphreys, Jean-Pierre Drege and Emile Burere, D. T. Suzuki, Robert Austin and Koichiro Ueda, Elmo Nauman, Osson the Younger [5]. I am just one of them. Imagine all the anonymous ones!

PART TWO

Abhidarma. Sanskrit term denoting the section of Buddhist canon that deals with metaphysics and philosophy.

Angya. The word designates the pilgrimage of a novice who wishes to join the monastery. His conventional dress consists of a wide bamboo rain hat, white cotton leggings, straw sandals and a shoulder bag for such things as his razor, bowls, books, etc. Such a journey is beautifully described in the poem *The Song of Angya,* written by Funyo Zensho during the Sung Dynasty.

Upon arrival at the monastery, the pilgrim must show a letter of introduction, if he has one, and then wait in the entrance court for several days until he is admitted. Upon admission, he is on probation for a bit longer, until he is called into the meditation hall where he bows before the shrine or statue and is then introduced to the brethren.

The pilgrimage is in itself valuable. The facing and overcoming of personal and bodily difficulties, including the whims of the weather, are an awakening and strengthening on the one hand, while the variegated beauties of nature and the constant encounters with different persons and human activities are culturally beneficial, on the other. It is on the pilgrimage itself, not in the visit to the Zen Master, that one may experience the Satori, but then the pilgrimage must be continued without benefit or waiting for the Satori in the event that it was not experienced.

An Xingao. In some sources - *An-Shi-kao.* The first advocate of the Ch'an or meditation doctrine in China, about AD 150. A renowned translator of Buddhist books into Chinese, he was of Parthian origin. Legend has it that he was a prince who renounced the throne and became a monk. Had he lived some fifteen centuries later, he might have been one of the main characters in *The Book of Bamboo.*

Assam bamboo (Dendrocalamus hamiltonii). Comes from Assam. Because of its strong resemblance to the rhinoceros horn, the Assamese for centuries smuggled its polished version to China as rhinoceros horns. Greed unmasked their forgery: the swindlers "produced" too many and the trade collapsed. It had sold well

101

because in China it was believed to be a good aphrodisiac and a cure for impotence.

Bombu Zen. Ordinary meditation, with or without philosophic or religious purpose. It is sometimes used only for the good of the mind or the body. It helps the mind just as physical exercise helps the body. It is included within the term mushinjo.

Daikon. Japanese radish the size of sugar beet. Usually the most important product of the monastery, daikon was pickled and sold at the market.

Daimyo. Master, medieval estate owner in Japan.

Er Ya. Ancient Chinese dictionary, written thousands of years before Christ.

Hosso. In the 7th century Prince Shotoku Taishi (AD 572-622) officially extended protection to Buddhism. This led to the creation of as many as six new schools; of those six only Hosso, Kegon and Ritsu still exist today ("Today again!" exclaims Osson the Younger). The big sects of today (!) are of later origin.

The Hosso School was founded in 635 (Osson the Younger discovered that in the second half of the 20th century only some 40 Hosso temples would be left in Japan and he was not wrong). The sect followed the Fa-hsiang idealistic school founded in China by Hsuan-tsang, the great traveller.

Japan, the Tokugawa Period (1600-1868). First 100 years. During the Tokugawa regime, the only new Buddhist philosophy to emerge was Obaku Zen. Christian influence was declared undesirable:all Spaniards, Portuguese and other Europeans were repeatedly expelled from Japan (1624, 1639, 1640). Although there was a strong philosophical confrontation of thought, Confucianism can be said to have dominated this period (primarily in the intellectual sense).

This period saw the appearance of some very strange, interesting books: *The Catalogue of Vegetables* is attributed to Kaibara Ekken, although also mentioned is the name of Kao-Chung, a celebrated cook from one of the Rinzai monasteries, with whom the Zen Master Ts'ao, formerly the ruler known as Osson the Younger, studied the plant world. Nor is there proof of the supposed regular (secret) exchange of papers between this cook and Obuto Nissan, the keeper of the ruler's bamboo groves. Some pages in the Catalogue strongly evoke the style used by the great connoisseur of the tall reeds, Nissan. His death took with it, as is more than obvious, hundreds of pages of inscribed manuscripts about various themes. In the absence of enough facts, the book *How to Live Well* is attributed to Ekken as well, although a close study of the style points to another possible author: Sung Shan, the great expert on medicines, in Japan known under his samurai name Senzaki.

[FOOTNOTES TO INTERWORD]

1) The "People and Events" column in the daily paper *Politika* (January 29, 1988) carried in picture and word an item taken from *Die Zeit* about an interesting discovery by a German zoologist, Bernhard Mayer from Ruhr University in Bochum. While in the jungles of Madagascar he came upon an unknown species of primate, and named it the Golden Bamboo Lemur (it is a scientific curiosity that the last new primate to be discovered was in 1930). Judging by the photograph, he was a real beauty: his black face was framed by a "mask the colour of gold," the young fellow was about 80 centimetres tall and weighed about 12 kilograms. (The item contained an error about his weight: an unnecessary period made him 1.2 kg. light). The second half of his name was taken from his feeding habits because he ate only bamboo. His body was like an upright bear's on a diet, and his face like that of the front line of mammals: a monkey's and a man's.

2) The *Book of Teacher Lie* (completed in about AD 380) contains an interesting dialogue between semi-invented characters. At one point Tang (the high king) of the Shang dynasty asks Xi Ji: "In the beginning did some things exist?" Xi Ji replies: "If things did not exist then, how can they exist today? *If later generations were to claim that things did not exist in our time, would they be right?*"

(italics by V.B.). Tang says: "Do things then not have either their before or their after?" To which Xi Ji replies: "There are no lines demarking where things begin and where they end. The beginning (of one thing) can be considered the end (of another); the end (of one) can be considered the beginning (of the next). Who can exactly distinguish between these two cycles? We cannot know what comes after all things or before all events."

3) M. Granet: *La Pensêe Chinoise*, Paris, 1934, p.86.

4) Within the theory of two basic natural forces, yin and yang, naturalists developed a system of five elements. Apart from the said wood and fire, there are earth, metal and water. For more details see: W. S. Soothill: *The Hall of Light, A Study in Early Christian Kinship*, London, 1951, p.30, and M. Granet's famous study: *Le Dêpot de l'Enfant sur le Sol*, first published in "Revue Archeologique", 1922 (5eme ser.) 14, 10, and then in "Etudes Sociologiques sur la Chine", Paris, 1953, p. 159.

5) Seven books that have stood the test of time long enough to be accepted:
a) Ernest Wood: *Zen Dictionary*, Penguin Books, London, 1963.
b) T. O. Ling: *A Dictionary of Buddhism*, Charles Scribner's Sons, New York, 1972.
c) Christmas Humphreys: *Buddhism (A Brief Glossary...)*, Penguin Books, London, 1972.
d) Jean-Pierre Drege: *La Route de la Soie*, Jugoslovenska revija, Motovun, 1986.
e) Daisetz T. Suzuki: *Zen and Japanese Culture*, Princeton University Press, New York, 1973.
f) Robert Austin, Koichiro Ueda: *Bamboo*, Weatherhill, New York, Tokyo, 1981.
g) St Elmo Nauman, Jr.: *Dictionary of Asian Philosophies*, Routledge and Kegan Paul, London, 1979.

Ian Holmes
TUNISIAN BLUES

"Have you found Tunisian boys have the best cocks?"

Egyptian music whirled around ceiling fans that didn't, in a bar in the ancient Tunisian city of Kairouan. I took a drag on his hookah and explained my preference. His eyes looked saddened. They were like the sticky almond cakes sold in the souk outside. Maybe our visit to the hamman, with all its dousing and pummelling amid steam, grunts and clanking metal buckets had given him the wrong impression.

At my hotel in the Medina the manager was a worried man. He had come up to my room and rapped urgently on its blue wooden door.

"Those boys you came with. Be careful!"

"I'm sorry?" I blinked, blinded by sun after the darkness of my room.

"You did not tip them. You must."

"They did nothing. I met them at the gate."

He looked very troubled: "They are members of the local mafia."

"What!?"

"Be careful, my friend. You are a stranger here. There will be trouble."

There had been trouble ever since I arrived in Israel to begin my journey west across Egypt and North Africa. A questionable itinerary? So it seemed to Tel Aviv airport's Head of Security. His eyes are the coldest place I've ever travelled. A detailed examination of your luggage makes you feel exposed; one of your body, considerably more so. It's not kid gloves those guys use, but rubber ones. The only thing 'tip-toe' about the whole process was my reaction to having a metal detector passed beneath my balls. It looked like a cross between a Kalashnikov and a Clarks' shoe gauge.

I'd explained that I was following up a story. A story once told me on a cargo boat out of Algiers by a deserter from the French Foreign Legion. Or rather, he had gone AWOL to try to get to his daughter's wedding in the Cotswolds the following week. A deep scar pitted the hand with which he'd gripped the boat's rail. He had told me about life in the desert, and about how his hand had been knived to the table at breakfast one day, in the scramble for the morning's bread.

From Kairouan I travelled to Douz. It is one of the last small sandy villages on the edge of the Sahara's Great Eastern Erg in south-west Tunisia. There, this morning, I stumbled upon the bakery. In a dark stone back room freshly baked bread was shovelled from a brick oven onto a wooden bench. Tousled kids gathered up in old newspaper the too hot to handle cobs, threw down their millemes and scurried out into the brilliant sun. Two cobs fell and rolled to dark corners. Thinking hygiene, not hunger, I hesitated. All bright orange polka dots and dusty black hair, a young girl scampered in, retrieved them, and hurried out. I'd had no chance, and was left wide-eyed and breadless.

It was on the road to Douz, hitching a ride in the back of a goat truck, that I met Sara and Gregoria. She was a big-eyed Portabelle looking for Bedouin bric-a-brac; he a German who had left behind an Islington squat and a promising career as a juggler of frying pans and kitchen utensils outside a restaurant in Piccadilly's Trocadero. We agreed to hire a Land Cruiser and guide to travel the 150km across the Sahara to the oasis of Ksar Ghilane. The fort there was once a desert outpost for the Romans, and the Foreign Legion. Maybe I could experience for myself some of what had been described to me years before.

All but one guide had refused to take us this trans-desert route owing to dangerous conditions caused by recent winds. Only minutes after we started southwards, our track petered into windswept dunes.

"*C'est la porte du Sahara,*" Adel our guide proudly announced as we sank deep into our first drift. Engine revving, wheels spinning, we laid tracks, shoved and shovelled while Adel showed Sara the width of his smiles, and explained how he and his Italian boss planned to open a chain of fast food joints across the Sahara: "Tourists here don't want cous-cous, tagine... Pah!" He spat the words out. "We will give them pasta, lasagne... and pizza! Soon. Next year maybe we will do this!"

For several weeks I'd been travelling through parched villages bordering the desert, where thick heat stacks crates high in the small shops whose stone walls' cool slivers of shadow are beaded with people, and with scrawny cats hanging out their pink tongues.

In one such village a birdseller, sitting beneath a picture of smiling Saddam, had explained to me how Iraq won the war. The birds tied to his wrists bounced up and down with every gesture.

In another, in a late-night café, a group of kids invited me to play table football. I was five dinar down (about five pounds) before I realised that my partner, my goalkeeper, was completely blind.

Recollection of days blisters with heat. But I won't forget how a guide at Tamerza offered to take me around the remains of a

Berber village only to lead me via a tangled oasis - a sort of playground for scorpions and snakes - where he suggested we sat and rested, his hand first patting, then stroking up my bare thigh. And there was the afternoon I was invited for mint tea at a house in a remote. silent village in the Khroumirie Mountains. My host was a friendly young Tunisian I had sat next to on the bus. After a glass or two, he brought out samples of the locally made jewelry he sold in the towns, and offered to exchange some for my shirt. My favourite Calvin Klein shirt. It had been a present from a girl called Suzie, who I'd met travelling the West Coast the year before. I declined. He, and then his brothers, became more demanding. I offered other exchanges. Their gestures and voices became more emphatic. They stood between me and the door, more practised at this than me, and argued until there seemed only one safe conclusion. Suzie, I'm sorry.

My partner had stayed in Cairo, though only partly from choice. By Cairo I mean Cairo Hospital, as he'd developed an unidentified fever. Whatever it was, it arrived the night we shared a single room in a Cairo hotel that proudly publicized that it was not suitable for westerners. But it was late, we were exhausted in a strange, hectic city, and everywhere else was full. There was no plumbing - you could smell that from the street outside - but this had not stopped previous guests from behaving as though there was. We had to step over boys sleeping in the corridor outside our room. By the door was one whose mouth had dropped open in sleep. It was full of flies. We lay awake, putting bets on giant cockroaches racing round the walls, and that night Giles contracted his fever.

Cattle pass more quickly than transport through this region's baking hot bus stations. Trapped on a bus to Tripoli I'd sat for seven hours next to a Libyan student intent on discussing every detail of an imaginary, great, final battle between the armies of the east and west, fought somewhere over the Mediterranean. He said it was something he thought about a lot. The woman opposite us had been sick over my rucksack. I offered her my water bottle, and missed my stop as in the crush to fit more than 124 people (I counted) onto a 50-seater bus, a baby was passed over everybody's heads and given me to hold. Finding the right French vowel sounds was like drawing rocks from a dry well.

To compensate for our unpromising Saharan entrance, Adel put on a tape of his girl-friend tunelessly singing Simon and Garfunkel - she spoke no English and was tone deaf - while we were shaken, rattled and rolled by the Land Cruiser's bucking and diving over undulating dunes, any one of which if misjudged would cause us to sink into drifts. In the rear-view mirror, rolling sand and sky violently slewed with every turn, and the distant Tebaga Mountains frowned through the dust we trailed.

Our route of invisible tracks took us away from the lighter, sensuously smooth sloping sands and gentler skies of El-Faouar and Sabria, the very last stranded Tunisian oases, home to the nomadic Ghrib tribe with their black tents and mud and palm huts, and on into a more deeply-coloured landscape of sandy scrubbery scorched brittle beneath an intense Tunisian-blue sky.

We passed wild camels' galloping geometry. Desert larks flew up before the bonnet. They flashed yellow, white and black, swooping and gliding. Lizards scooted across our path. Beside the print marks of gazelles and desert foxes their squiggled tracks read like the Koran etched in stone in Kairouan's Great Mosque.

The sand we now sank into was a fine orange powder. So fine it seemed fluid. It was wind-rippled into meringue-like ridges, or sent scudding in patches across the dunes like moments of sunlight from behind moving clouds.

In such terrain we rested at sunset by a Bedouin watering-hole, a triangle of poles set over a simple well, to watch a molten amber sun sink in seconds. And the most tender crepuscular pink ripen with settling dusk. A Bedouin family crouched around the well. The womenfolk gathered their privacy in the folds of their clothes. Their young boy brought over an animal skin of water with which he carefully filled our bottles.

In darkness we rolled on. Our headlights haphazardly swept the sandy floor, lighting shoals of dunes patterned like fish scales and spines, their crests like waves. Night had only us to engulf. The rasping flare of my lonely match was lost as soon as lit, smothered in her black burnous.

When suddenly we arrived, Ksar Ghilane's oasis curled her dark green back against the encroaching sands and whispered cool watery promises. As we ate by a campfire I arranged to hire a camel at sunrise and ride the few kilometres to the Foreign Legion fort. Over a simple breakfast of figs, melon, cheese and bread I would watch the land awake. Already I sensed what a place of absence and desolation I would find. A baked husk of the sun and sweat filled lives that must have trickled away within its walls, grain by grain. As slowly as the walls themselves turned to sand.

A distant daughter's wedding might well play on a man's mind in such a place, his soul's every cranny silted with sand. A place where rigorous military exercise was as inconceivable as the vastness of the landscape. A landscape of such sculpted beauty, such mystical allure. Though I suspect that my cargo boat companion never made it to the wedding photographs, as he was led aside by two plain clothes men at Marseille Passport Control. An allure of a rather less mystical kind.

Then, after we had eaten, we swam in a pool of deliciously warm spring water, surrounded by myriad birds' and insects' nightcalls. Any worries over what slippery shapes slid about the water with us were forgotten as I floated beneath a sky whose stars jostled for space. And through the palms, a full moon hung only inches above ground.

The few local Africans who tended the oasis sat around chatting over mint tea. One began to beat on some drums. Others started clapping in time. Someone was playing a bamboo pipe, and soon they were all singing dark rich rhythms. Their songs and laughter rang around this small pool of life, this drop in an ocean of sand. We had all long forgotten the day's heat, hassle and dust. In the cool of night those boys were just happily singing, happily singing Tunisian Blues.

Naguib Mahfouz
HANZAL AND THE POLICEMAN

*Translated by Azza Kararah
and revised by David Kirkhaus*

The sound of heavy footsteps reverberated ominously within his breast, and the 'humph' that accompanied it was a forewarning of pain and trouble. It was the police-constable approaching in the dark. He longed to run away, but could not. With great difficulty he managed to lift himself up and to throw his weight against the wall at the corner of the lane. He staggered. At any moment now he might collapse. With difficulty he opened his eyes and focused them in the direction of his oncoming doom. Several times he tried to move in the dark but could not, and his thoughts and recollections were all scattered. His face - colourless, dusty and rugged - looked numb by the light of the street lamp. He wore nothing but the remains of a torn gallabeyya and his frenzied entrails burnt with a craving for the forbidden shot.

"Hanzal, come here..."

That fateful call, that was followed by blows and kicks. In a desperate, sickly voice he pleaded.

"Constable, have mercy on me, for God's sake."

He stood facing him, blocking the light of the street lamp, with his gun hanging from his shoulder. Hanzal pressed himself harder against the wall of Shanafiry Lane. In his fear, he tried to resist the faintness that threatened to overcome him; he whined miserably. But what was the matter? Why did the policeman not shout and scold and strike?

113

"Have you had the shot?"

"No, I swear I haven't."

"But you're in a stupor, or you seem to be."

"That's because I haven't taken it."

"Come with me, the officer wants you."

There came a sigh from his maddened, famished breast.

"I beg you..." he cried.

But the hand that was laid on his shoulder was not an iron grip, nor was it a policeman's clutch; it was a human hand. Surprised, Hanzal could not utter a word, so the policeman said: "Come on, don't be afraid."

"I've done nothing wrong!"

He led him along gently and whispered soothingly: "You'll find that everything's all right. Don't be afraid."

He stood in the superintendent's room, about a yard away from the door, which was closed behind him. He could neither step forward nor raise his eyes and meet the glance that would be directed towards him from a stern face. The bright light shone on his mud-bespattered and almost naked body. Here, between the smooth white walls and the imposing furniture, he appeared like something that time had forgotten. A thunderbolt was what Hanzal expected, but to his surprise the commissioner's tone was a human one. Everything was surprising that night.

"Good evening, Hanzal. Sit down."

God in heaven! What on earth was happening?

"Heaven forbid, sir. I am your unworthy servant."

But the officer cast a reproving look at him and pointed a peremptory finger at a leather armchair. He hesitated for a long while, but seeing that there was nothing for it he gave in and perched himself on the edge of the chair with eyes fixed on his dusty feet. They looked so huge, like the feet of a statue, under their layers of grime. Hanzal could still not really believe these signs of courtesy, and in an obsequious voice he said: "Captain, sir, I'm a poor man with a lot that can be held against me, but my misery is far greater than my wrongdoings... and in God's eyes mercy is a higher thing than justice."

The officer retorted in a voice that was both gentle and

earnest: "Don't worry, Hanzal. I know your wrongdoings are very many, but your sufferings are greater. You know your wrongdoings best.... The constable is not to be blamed for his cruelty to you, for the law is the law. But new conditions call for a change of treatment... a change in everything. As for us, it is true we are policemen, but we are also human."

Full of bewilderment he kept on gazing in wonder at the office while trying very hard to overcome his feeling of faintness. The man cast a pitying glance at him. "Trust in me, Hanzal," he said. "You must believe everything you hear and everything you see. You cannot concentrate because you have not had your shot. All your money is gone, and you have not had your shot. The poison-pedlar has no mercy and wants his price in advance. But you will be cured of all this...."

"I'm a wretch," Hanzal replied, whimpering. "All my life has been sheer bad luck. I used to be strong and now I'm weak. I was a trader and now I'm bankrupt, I've loved and suffered, I've become an addict and a beggar."

'You'll leave the sanatorium a better man and then we shall meet again."

In the yard of the police station he was surrounded by a group of policemen. Instinctively, from habit, he cowered as though to avoid a blow. Their thick lips broke into smiles under wayward moustaches.

"You!"

"Yes, Hanzal. Everything has changed."

"Get well soon, Hanzal."

"Let bygones be bygones."

He was carried away half-asleep and soon gave in altogether, in the carriage that lulled him to infinity. He opened his eyes in a strange room; it was dazzling white and brilliantly lit. He saw a strange face bending over him and he felt weak and sick, afraid and utterly lonely.

"The shot, the shot, Uncle Matbouli!" he humbly begged.

A soft laugh tickled his ear and a pungent smell penetrated his nose. He suffered a devastating hunger in his head and senses; the sides of his head were splitting, then he lost consciousness.

Hanzal left the sanatorium a new man, just as the police officer had promised. His features glowed for the first time and he swaggered along in a voluminous white gallabeyya. He had shaved his beard and his moustache, and looked healthy and strong once more. He wore bright yellow slippers, while the lion tattooed on his wrist was visible again, as well as the bird on his temple under the ornate turban. A policeman walked along with him, like a friend. Everything was friendly. His clear, dark skin gleamed in the sun. He had to laugh; surely, he said to himself, he must have lost weight with all this cleaning. He was wide awake, he could see, he could hear; he loved the police constable and he no longer felt that gnawing pain inside him. He was so full of self-confidence that he felt he could fly. He had faith in everything around him and was not surprised when police constables came towards him and congratulated him. There, in the yard of the police station, they all crowded round him and cordially shook him by the hand. He was not over-surprised either when he saw the police officer standing up to greet him. He was deeply moved and humbly he stooped forward in order to kiss the officer's hand. But he was received with open arms and embraced with kindness. He broke down with bashfulness and gratitude and his eyes overflowed with tears. The man seated him in the armchair and then went back to his own seat behind the desk. He gave a gentle, clear laugh: "Congratulations on your recovery," he said.

Hanzal's eyes swam with unshed tears.

"Now you can start afresh," the officer went on.

His tears flowed freely: "Thanks be to God and to you," he answered.

"Do not exaggerate. Thanks are due to God alone."

The officer then opened a book in front of him and with a pen he wrote something at the top of the white sheet; quietly, with a look in his eyes, as deep as moonlight, he said, "State your wishes, Hanzal." Hanzal was confused and could not reply. His lips moved and with them his uncouth moustache, but he remained tongue-tied. The officer urged him on, "State your wishes, Hanzal. That is an order," he was saying.

"But..."

"No buts - state your wishes."

He hesitated a while, then said, "All I want is God's protection."

"Make yourself clear. State your wishes. That is an order."

Hanzal remembered a mother's prayer, tales at night, tunes on the fiddle; then he chuckled, "I used to go around the streets with a fruit cart," he said.

"A fruit shop in the Hussainia," the officer said. He wrote in his book: double shelves, electric light for better display...

In a daze Hanzal enquired, "And the money?"

"Do not trouble yourself, that is our responsibility and a matter for the public concern. Speak up and state your wishes. That is an order."

Hanzal found new courage which he drew from his new personality and from the fruit shop.

"Saneyya Bayoumi, who sells liver," he said in a shaking voice. "The truth..."

The officer interrupted while his hand continued to write: "No need to explain, everything is known, known to the policeman at the station and by all the other police. Known also to the watchman in the market place. Saneyya is a bold and pretty girl, and she is not yet married in spite of all that has taken place. There was a time when she was more harm to you than the heroin you were taking. And the more cruel she became, the worse your condition grew. She has deserted you, but she will come back to you. Let it be a fruit and liver shop. There will be nothing else like it in the Hussainia. Just like a very exclusive grocer's. Anything else?"

Greatly moved, he bent his head and, as in a dream, he saw green pastures in which red, purple-fringed flowers grew; and in his ears a tune sounded, repeating the refrain *Tell Me My Heart's Desire*. But then he saw a dark blur, like a cloud of flies, and his whole body winced.

"I fear, sir," he said, pitifully, "this friendliness of the police may not last; because not the least of my miseries, in the past, was the way the police behaved. They were always after me and my cart, with reason or without; they'd confiscate my stock and beat me up. As for that business over Saneyya, it was Constable Hassouna who first began to turn her head."

The pleasant, clear laugh rose again.

"You will not find one enemy among the police," the officer retorted, in a tone that left no room for doubt. "From now on, and for good, they will be your faithful friends. State your wishes, Hanzal. That is an order."

Hanzal felt an intoxicating courage that had never been his, even in the days of his youthful exploits. A courage that was backed by a fruit and liver shop, by the love of Saneyya and the friendship of the police.

"There's many poor like me," he said, "and you, sir, you probably don't know them."

"I know everything," the officer broke in, though his hand never stopped writing. "Tell us who they are and every one of them will have his shop, his woman and the friendship of the police. All this will come true, and so state your wishes. That is an order."

Hanzal laughed very loud and pressed his hands hard together.

"This is too much like a dream," he said.

"Reality is a kind of dream; dreams are a kind of reality. State your wishes. That is an order."

He took a deep, full, confident breath.

"How many prisoners really deserve to be in prison?" he said, musingly.

The officer answered while his hand still continued to run over the paper: "Everyone who does not really deserve prison will be let out, even if it leaves the prison empty."

Full of exaltation, Hanzal cried out: "Long live justice! Long live the Superintendent!"

The courtyard of Hanzal's house in Shanafiry Lane then witnessed a party of a unique kind, at which the Superintendent and the constables, the poor and the one-tim jailbirds were there. Saneyya wore an orange dress with a green shawl round her shoulders so that no part of her plump body was visible, except a wrist adorned with a golden bracelet and an ankle encircled by a silver bangle with dangling crescents. She herself served the

drinks, tamarind and karkadeh, while, in a corner, a band with a touch of Mohammed Ali Street blared out its welcome. They all enjoyed their freedom; even the policemen danced and sang under the eyes of their superior officer. Then a Koran-reciter rose amidst his followers and started a chant in praise of the Prophet:
With his advent came the light of truth.

The poor, the ex-convicts and the policemen, all sighed with satisfaction and Saneyya's joyous trilling-cry sounded like the descant of a reed pipe. Then finally, at the close of the festivities, the police officer stood up and addressed them all, and said: "It never rains but it pours... and these are only the first drops. Goodnight to you all."

Once more, Saneyya uttered her trilling-cry and the guests began to leave. The day was just breaking, the roosters glorified God and the silence glorified Him too.

Hanzal stretched himself on a couch to rest, and Saneyya sat down by his head and toyed with the forelock of his hair. He was happy, peaceful and contented, and wished that things would remain as they were for ever.

"You're the source of all things good," he said gently.

Her fingers went down to his temple as though she wished to feed the bird that was tattooed there. He went on to say: "I don't think of all that's happened as miraculous. The real miracle is that your heart should have softened after being..."

Her hand slipped down to his cheek, then to his chin and finally rested at his throat. He surrendered himself to her caresses and in the depths of his heart he longed for this moment never to end. But, suddenly, he became aware of a strange feeling, a kind of pressure on his throat, a pressure too great for any kind of fondling. He wanted to ask her not to press so hard, but his voice would not come out and still the pressure increased. He stretched out his hand to remove hers from his neck but he felt as though a nightmare or incubus were pressing him down; he felt as though a heavy weight, a sandbag or part of a wall, had fallen on his head. He wanted to cry out, to stand up, to move, but could not. He turned his head brusquely to get rid of this torture and scraped it against the couch, or rather against something that felt like the

119

ground - dust and mud. A strange feeling overwhelmed him, new in its nature, its flavour, the depth of its sadness. He heard a well-known, mocking voice shouting at him.

"And so now you go to sleep in the middle of the road!"

How very like the police constable's voice this sounded. The old police constable with his rough voice that was always a forewarning of trouble. He felt suffocated. Saneyya's hand knew no mercy. Suddenly the wall was lifted from his chest and he sat up moaning in the dark. He seemed to make out the shadow of a giant blocking the light of the street lamp and towering up towards the stars. The cocks of dawn were crowing and a rifle appeared behind the shoulder of this spectre. The pain upon his chest gave way when the heavy boot was lifted from it.

"Constable," he called out, "what of the police superintendent's promises?"

The policeman kicked Hanzal savagely.

"The Superintendent's promise!" he cried. "You crazy junky... come on, to the station."

Hanzal looked around in terror and bewilderment; and all he found was a slumbering street, an enveloping darkness, a silence... no party, no trace of a party... no Saneyya... nothing.

Naguib Mahfouz
THE MOSQUE IN THE
NARROW LANE

Translated by Nadia Farag,
revised by Josephine Wahba

It was time for the afternoon address and, as usual, only one outsider was present. Ever since the arrival of Sheikh Abdu Rabbuh as Imam of the Mosque, only *Am* [1] Hassanein, the vendor of sugar-cane juice, had come to hear him at that time of day. Out of respect for the idea of a sermon and deference to the Imam, the muezzin and the mosque servant made a habit of coming too. One might have expected Sheikh Abdu Rabbuh to be vexed by this, but with time, the Sheikh had resigned himself. Perhaps, too, he had expected a worse plight when he was first appointed to this mosque on the outskirts of the red light district. He had resented the transfer and had tried to have it rescinded, or changed to an appointment elsewhere, but, in the end, very much against his wish, he had been obliged to accept the post, and submit, as a concomitant, to the derision of his rivals, and the banter of his friends.

And who would come to the sermon? The mosque stood at the crossroads of two lanes: one was an alley noted for the debauchery that occurred there, and the other housed procurors, pimps and narcotics dealers. It seemed that the only pious man in the whole quarter, or even the only normally decent man, was Am Hassanein, the fruit-juice man. For a long time, the Sheikh had shuddered every time he chanced to look up the alleys, as if he

121

feared the contact with lewdness and crime would contaminate his soul if he were to breathe too deeply. In spite of all this he delivered his sermons with a regularity which was paired by Am Hassanein's regularity in attendance. He once said to the juice vendor: "You'll soon become an Imam yourself, and people will be quoting you as an example and an authority." The old man smiled timidly, "Oh! I have still so much to learn..."

The homily that evening was on purity of conscience, considered as the basis of sincerity and integrity in a man's dealings with himself and with others, and with the act of contrition as a commendable practice for starting the day. Am Hassanein listened intently as usual. But he rarely asked questions, except for an occasional enquiry about the meaning of a verse in the Koran, or the practice of the ordinances.

From the southern window of the mosque, looking in the direction of prayer, one had a full view of the lanes were the brothels were situated. It was a long and narrow lane, crooked in parts, with doors of dilapidated houses and cafes on both sides. It had a strangely stirring effect on the senses. At this time of day the district seemed to wake up and stretch as if after a long sleep, and to prepare for the evening. People spattered the ground with water from pails, doors were opened furtively in answer to knockings which were in fact pre-arranged signals; chairs were set in order in cafes; women appeared at the windows, smartening themselves up between snatches of conversation; brazen laughter echoed in the air; incense burned in hallways. A woman could be heard crying, with the voice of the *madame* urging her to pull herself together, in order that they might not lose more money: it was enough that her pimp had lost his life in a brawl. Another woman laughed hysterically because she was unable to forget her friend who had been killed as she sat next to her. A gruff voice was heard to say indignantly: "Even a European! Who would have expected it! How could a European have ditched Fardos! Fleeced her of a hundred pounds and then disappeared."

Voices rehearsed an obscene song, which was to be performed later. At the end of the lane a fight was taking place; it began with a simple exchange of words and ended with chairs being thrown. Libliba slipped out and sat in the doorway of the nearest house. A street lamp had already been lit. One could feel the lane coming to life.

One day, Sheikh Abdu Rabbuh was summoned by telephone to the office of the Inspector General in charge of Religious Affairs. He was informed that there was to be a general meeting of all imams. Although this was not very unusual, particularly in the circumstances which preceded the summons, the Sheikh wondered anxiously what lay behind it. The Inspector General was a formidable figure who derived his importance from a close family connection with a certain high official whose name was anathema to everyone. He appointed and dismissed ministers at will and abused the institutions which were venerated by the common people. In his presence, the imams were helpless and would no doubt incur his anger for the slightest thing. The Sheikh murmured a brief prayer of invocation, and prepared himself for the meeting as best he could. He put on a black and almost new kaftan, wound his turban round his head, and set off, trusting in God.

He found the corridor in front of the Inspector's room as crowded as if (to use his own expression) it had been the Day of Resurrection. The imams chatted together and asked each other what it was all about. Finally the large door opened and they were allowed to enter the spacious office, filling it to overflowing. The Inspector received them in a dignified and formal manner and listened to the flood of prepared panegyric with a constrained air, trying to suppress an enigmatic smile. When the recitation of complaints ended there was a moment of heavy silence. The mood of expectancy grew more intense: he shifted his glance from face to face. At last, he replied: he responded tersely to their greetings and expressed his confidence that they would live up to the good opinion he had of them. Then, pointing to the photograph above his head, he said: "It is because of the duties we owe him and the Royal family that we are holding this meeting."

Many of those present felt uneasy, but they did not lose their composure. The Inspector General went on: "The firm bond that unites you to him is something that can hardly be expressed in words. It is a mutual loyalty, rooted firmly in our history."

The listeners' faces radiated approval, in order to conceal their inner distress, and the official continued: "... and now, in the face of this storm which is sweeping the country, he is calling upon your loyalty..."

The inward agitation increased.

"... to enlighten the people. You must expose all impostors and agitators in order that the rightful ruler may be firmly established in power."

He continued relentlessly, elaborating upon this theme, then, scrutinising the faces before him, asked if there were any questions or comments. There was a silence, until one imam, bolder then the rest, pointed out that the inspector had indeed admirably expressed their own inner feelings. If it had not been for their fear of acting without instructions they would already have hastened, of their own accord, to carry out the duties which they were now being called upon to perform. As soon as the inspector began to speak, Sheikh Abdu Rabbuh realised to his relief that they had not been brought here to give an account of their own actions, or to have their attitudes investigated, but rather that the authorities were appealing to them for help. Perhaps even some genuine move to raise their salaries and pensions might result. But his feeling of uneasiness soon returned, just as a wave that beats upon a clear sandy shore inevitably falls back seawards in a thin line of foam. He realised with perfect clarity what he would undoubtedly be forced to say in the Friday sermon: things which went against his conscience and were hated by the people. He felt certain that many of the others shared his feelings and were passing through the same crisis - but what could they do? He went back to the mosque brooding over this new anxiety.

Shaldam, the pimp, a well-known figure in the district, was at that moment holding forth to a gathering of his assistants in the Welcome Bar which stood only a few steps away from the mosque. He seemed to be in a towering rage which augmented with every glass of red wine.

"Nabawiyya - the crazy fool - is in love," he roared, "with that blasted little twerp Hassan. I'm sure of it!"

"Perhaps she just thinks of him as a client, no more than a client..." said one of his cronies, trying to pacify him.

Shaldam struck the table with an iron fist which scattered the lupin seeds and salted peanuts that were being offered as refreshment.

"No!" he said savagely, "he lays her for free. I'm sure of it: as sure as I am that my dagger never misses. He doesn't pay a single millieme and she gives him all kinds of presents."

The faces mirrored a feeling of loathing and the drunken eyes expressed a readiness to cooperate.

"The bloody swine usually comes in when the bitch is doing her turn," he added. "Wait for him to arrive then start a row - leave the rest to me."

They emptied their wine glasses, their eyes reflecting an ominous determination to act.

After the evening prayer, Sheikh Abdu Rabbuh received a visit from two of his college friends, the Imam Khalid and the Imam Mubarak; they informed him gloomily that some of the imams had been dismissed from their posts for refusing to take part in the campaign.

"Places of worship indeed," murmured Khalid angrily. "They were not built for political controversy and not, in any case, to uphold tyranny."

Abdu Rabbuh felt a fresh pang and he retorted with the conventional phrase: "Do you want us to be reduced to starvation? Do you?"

A heavy silence fell. Sheikh Rabbuh refused to admit defeat and in order to save his face in front of his friends he pretended to be convinced: "What you consider a controversial point may be the actual truth..."

Khalid, quite amazed at the Sheikh's reversal of attitude, withdrew from the discussion; Mubarak burst out in his usual rash way: "In that case we shall be doing away with the Islamic precept which tells us to teach what is commendable and to condemn what is evil."

Abdu Rabbuh realised that he was going against his own conscience and this made him all the more angry with Mubarak:

"No," he said, "we shall be reviving the Islamic precept that calls for obedience to God and His prophet *and* to the secular authorities."

Mubarak retorted with tremendous indignation: "And would you call these people *authorities?*"

"Tell me," said Abdu Rabbuh defiantly, "are you really going to refuse to deliver the sermon?"

Mubarak rose and walked away angrily, followed soon after by Khalid. The Sheikh cursed them as he cursed his own conscience.

Around midnight the courtyard of the seventh house on the right-hand side filled up with drunks. They sat on wooden chairs round a sanded area lit by a pressure-lamp; inside the circle, Nabawiyya was dancing. She wore a pink nightgown, holding in her right hand a quarter-staff wound with a ribbon studded with flowers. Hands clapped rhythmically and brutish cries of rapture rose from drunken mouths. The pimps sneaked into the yard and placed themselves in various corners, waiting. Shaldam crouched at the foot of the stairs, his eyes fixed on the entrance.

Hassan made his appearance; his hair was smoothed down and he wore a radiant smile on his face. Shaldam darted vicious glances at him. The newcomer stood watching Nabawiyya. As soon as she saw him she acknowledged his presence with a large smile, a specially enticing wiggle of her belly, and a wink. Hassan put on a proprietorial air, looked for an empty seat and sat down. Shaldam's blood boiled. His fingers twitched. He gave a little whistle. At once, two of his gang began a sham fight. The others intervened and the fight spread, growing more and more violent. The drunkards, taken by surprise, rose drowsily and made quickly for the door. A chair flew at the pressure-lamp, shattering it: darkness fell heavily on the place. Screams blended with curses and the stamping and shuffling of feet. In the middle of the fray, out of the darkness, a woman's shriek pierced the tumult, followed by a man's agonised cry. The yard was soon empty, except for two bodies which lay in the silent darkness under a cloud of dust.

*   *   *

The following day was Friday. When the time for noon prayers arrived, the mosque was crowded with worshippers. On Fridays, in contrast to weekdays, people came to the mosque from distant parts of cairo, such as El Khazindar and El Ataba. After the recital of the Koran, Sheikh Abdu Rabbuh stood up to deliver the sermon. The congregation were more astonished than ever he could have predicted, at the political bent of this sermon. They listened and received the rhymed phrases about obedience and the duty of allegiance with both disbelief and irritation. And when the speaker began to condemn the revolutionaries, saying that in inciting the people to revolt they were only fostering their own interests, a general murmur filled the mosque; voices rose in indignant protest, and some cursed the imam. Upon this, the police informers who had sneaked in among the worshippers fell upon the most vociferous dissidents and led them away amidst scenes of angry protest. Many people walked out of the mosque; the imam led the rest of the congregation in prayer. It was a sad and gloomy prayer.

Meanwhile, in the second house on the left-hand side of the lane, Samara was entertaining a new customer in her room. She sat on the edge of the bed, half-undressed, and reached for a wedge of cucumber from a glass which was half-full of water and crunched it between her teeth. On a chair near the bed sat the client, with his coat off, drinking brandy from a bottle. His gaze wandered absent-mindedly over the bare room and settled on Samara. He put the bottle to her lips, let her take a mouthful, then drew it away. The recitation of the Koran coming from the mosque reached his ear. A ghost of a smile appeared on his face. He lowered his eyes and muttered irritably: "Why did they have to build a mosque here? Was there nowhere else?"

"This place is as good as any other," retorted Samara, nibbling at her cucumber.

He swallowed about two tots of brandy, and screwing up his eyes scrutinised her face: "Have you no fear of God, woman?"

"May God forgive us all..." she replied, rather piqued.

He laughed thinly and, reaching for a wedge of cucumber, thrust it whole into his mouth.

Abdu Rabbuh was now delivering his sermon. Samara's customer followed the words, nodding his head as he did so, and then began to smile sarcastically: "Old hypocrite!" he said, "listen to what he's saying!"

His gaze wandered over the room once more and settled on an old, faded picture of Saad Zaghloul [2]. He pointed to the picture and asked, "Do you know who that is?"

"Of course I do! Who doesn't?"

He emptied the bottle down his throat and said heavily: "So Samara's a patriot, and the Sheikh's a two-faced hypocrite."

"I do envy him," she sighed. "He makes a fortune just by saying a few words. But the likes of us can only earn a few piastres and that by the sweat of our bodies."

"They're nothing but a bunch of self-important men," he said sarcastically, "the kind they call 'respectable'. Not really different from you - but who's got the courage to say it?"

"Everybody knows who killed Nabawiyya, but who's got the courage to name him?"

He shook his head in sorrow: "Poor Nabawiyya!" he said. "Who did do it?"

"Shaldam, God rot his soul."

"Good God! Anyone who gives *him* away is asking for martyrdom. Thank God we're not the only sinners in the country."

"You're wasting a lot of time talking," she said, very annoyed by now.

Sheikh Abdu Rabbuh decided to exploit the situation at the mosque for his own advantage. He wrote a letter to the Ministry saying that he had been exposed to great danger because of his 'patriotic' sermon. He also managed to get his story into the press in a heavily exaggerated form, emphasising that police intervention had been needed to protect him and to arrest his assailants. He nourished vast hopes of promotion. However, when it was time for the afternoon homily there was not a single listener present. He looked across the lane into the fruit-juice shop and caught a glimpse of the owner at work. Thinking that Hassanein had forgotten about the lesson, he took a few steps outside the mosque and called out cheerfully: "The lesson, Am Hassanein..."

When he heard his name called out, the man automatically looked up, but he then turned his head away with determination, in a gesture of rejection. Abdu Rabbuh was ashamed, and was sorry he had called him. He went inside, heaping curses upon the man.

At daybreak, the muezzin climbed the minaret. It was still dark and cool and the full moon shone down in perfect stillness. No sooner had he begun his chant with the words "God is Great" than the air-raid siren burst out in a terrifying, broken howl. The muezzin's heart beat violently; he murmured a silent prayer and prepared himself for a renewal of the call as soon as the siren should stop. Ever since Italy had declared war on the Allies, the alert had become a common occurrence by night, but never developed into anything serious. Putting his heart into it the muezzin chanted, "There is no God but God," intoning the call in a fine voice. Suddenly there was an earth-shaking explosion and his voice died away. He stood chilled to the bone, his limbs trembling, staring blankly into the distance to where a red flame loomed. He took a few heavy steps towards the door, and went down the stairs with shaking knees. He reached the interior of the mosque in pitch darkness and directed his footsteps towards the imam and the mosque attendant, guiding himself by their whispers.

"It looks quite serious, my friend," he said in a quavering voice, "What are we going to do?"

"The public shelter's too far off," said the imam, his voice slightly hoarse, "and by now it must be filled with the rabble. The mosque is very solid. It'll make an excellent shelter."

They sat down in a corner and began to recite the Koran. From the outside quick footsteps reached them, shouts, agitated cries of advice, the creak of doors opening and closing. More explosions were heard, leaving nerves shattered and hearts beating in silence. The mosque servant suddenly cried out: "My family is at home, Your Reverence, and the house is rather rickety."

"Put your trust in God.... Don't move from your place," said the imam in a strangled voice.

A group of people rushed into the mosque. Some were heard to say: "This is the safest place..."

"It's rather serious tonight..." a rough, hoarse voice said.

The imam shuddered at the sound of the voice... the brute... surely his presence here was a portent of doom. Another group came in, larger than the first; and women's voices not unknown to the Sheikh were heard.

"The effect of the wine has quite worn off..."

The imam lost his temper. He jumped up and shouted in agitation: "Off with you to the public shelter. You must have some respect for the house of God. Off with you, all of you...."

A man's voice answered: "Your Reverence - shut up!"

A mocking peal of laughter burst out, to be drowned in a fresh explosion which deafened the ears and left them ringing. The mosque was filled with screams: the imam was terrorised. He yelled savagely as if he were addressing the bombs themselves: "Away with you... don't defile the house of God!"

"You ought to be ashamed of yourself," said a woman's voice.

"Go away!" screamed the imam, "The curse of God fall upon you..."

"This is the house of God, not your own house," the woman answered sharply.

Once again the man called out in coarse tones: "Do shut your mouth, Your Reverence, or I'll throttle you."

An outpour of sharp comments and biting remarks fell on the imam, and the muezzin whispered in his ear: "Don't answer, I beg of you."

Abdu Rabbuh said with great difficulty: "Do you think it right that the mosque should shelter the likes of these?"

"They have no choice," pleaded the muezzin. "Don't you know that this is a district of old houses? They can come tumbling down at a mere knock, let alone a rain of bombs."

The imam struck his palm with his fist.

"I wish I could put up with all these vicious rogues," he said.

130

"God must have a special reason for bringing them together here."

A bomb exploded. It seemed to their over-wrought senses that the explosion was in Midan el Khazindar. A flash of light lit up the courtyard of the mosque to disclose terrified figures almost immediately swallowed up in the blinding darkness.

Savage howls rent the air. The women shrieked. Even Sheikh Abdu Rabbuh screamed, unaware to himself. He lost his head and rushed blindly towards the entrance. The mosque attendant ran after him and tried to stop him, but Abdu Rabbuh pushed him away violently and shouted: "Follow me, both of you, before you perish."

He darted out, shrieking in a tremulous tone: "God undoubtedly has a design in bringing all these people together..." And he plunged into the thick darkness.

The air-raid lasted for another ten minutes, during which four more bombs were dropped. The city remained wrapped in silence for about another quarter of an hour, and then the All Clear sounded.

Faintly, with the dawn, the darkness dispelled; the morning light was an assurance of safety.

But the body of Sheikh Abdu Rabbuh was not discovered until after sunrise.

NOTES:

[1] *Am* - 'Uncle'
[2] Saad Zaghloul - Egyptian nationalist leader of the 1920s

Ibrahim al Kouni
THE MAIDEN'S VOW

Translated by Peter Clark

I

"Ghr... ghr... ghr... rqq... rqq."

She listened again. She strained her ears to identify the sound which was new to her and tried again to reproduce herself the language of the water.

"Lqq... lqq... lqq... lqq... lqq... lqq!"

She was delighted. This last sound satisfied her and she repeated it over and over again. She leant over the stream as it gushed into little rivulets that found a way between the rocks. It twisted round withered bushes that were scattered over the broad wadi bed.

A breeze, cool and humid, came from the north.

Rain.

The sky was cloudless in Hamada. Nonetheless the sun held back its power. To the north, its rays were restrained and the torment of the heat was more bearable. A tongue of the stream was lapping the tribes' grazing grounds by mid-day. Herdsmen shouted to each other. People gathered together and then spread out along the wadi bed savouring the sight of this miracle. Houses were abandoned as people went to set eyes on the stream - even the old women went. Children stripped off and crawled on hands and knees trying to swim in the shallow water. Many were cut by stones and thorns, and their mothers came to fish them out of the water.

"Take care," warned the old women. "Don't let up for a moment with this water. Jinns lurk in the background. There is a sting in its tail."

The younger generation had been denied the sight of a flood all their lives, hearing of it only in the legends of their elders. They were heedless and full of wonder.

Tazidirat belonged to this generation.

She had woken up early and was taking the sheep and goats down the slopes towards the wadi bed when she witnessed the miracle. Water a few inches deep was on land that had been punished by drought and the sun, deprived of the taste of water for decades and here it was flowing by. What amazed her most was the wonderful flood itself, so abundant that it gathered in some places and flowed, rushed down, poured down between rocks, around parched bushes and over the thirsty land.

God be praised!

She stood still, unable to move. She forgot herself. Speechless. In unknown territory. Clouds had not yet gathered. Not a single drop of water had fallen. Where could all this amount of water, enough to flood the thirsty wadi, have come from? A wadi, so voracious that she saw it swallow up a whole skinful of water in the twinkling of an eye.

Her grandmother had told her that the rains fell on the heights of Jabal Hasawana and Jabal Nafusa in the far north. Then they would come down in streams and pour into the wadis. These filled up and then the flood moved on to the southern plains. But she had never for a moment really believed these tales. She could not believe that the sky would bestow an amount of water that could cross these vast distances in Hamada without the thirsty land on the way taking it and absorbing it all.

And now here she was witnessing with her own eyes this fairy tale come true. Unbelievable.

Her heart was still beating wildly when she came to the wadi's brink and gazed down at the busy flood as it swept away animal droppings and tufts of grass. It swamped the stones and coiled playfully round shrubs.

She heard the water's gurgle for the first time.

She could not believe that either.

She took a few steps nearer. She paused and then stretched

her hand out. She touched the water. She gave a shudder. A strange but sweet sensation took hold of her. She dipped her hand again into the water, cold, benevolent, gentle, strange.

She bent over the stream and listened to its language of mystery. She listened for a long time. Her heart continued to flutter. She looked up and saw the tribe approaching the wadi and spreading out over the rocky plain. She realised that the water was not a figment of her imagination. She leant again over the stream and listened to its strange rhythm.

Then she tried to imitate the sound.

Ghr... ghr... ghr... rqq... rqq... rqq... lqq... lqq... lqq.

II

They said famine had wiped out half the tribe during those years.

A few survived by clinging to a wretched life in the oases. Her father had left her with her grandmother and went to join a tribe in Hamada when drought in the desert joined forces with the enemy in the north. The Italians crushed resistance in the coastal area and began to raid the mountains, preparatory to penetrating the south. Her father shared his tribe's misfortunes and died of hunger before the Italians reached Hamada. Her mother who belonged to the Aifughas tribe also abandoned her before she was nine months old, by dying of some unknown plague.

They did not stay long in the oasis. The Italians seized the southern desert and battles raged in the sands of Zallaq. The resistance suffered terrible losses, forcing them to retreat south and take refuge in the desert sands. The road to the oases was thus open to the invaders.

Awful news reached them Just a few days before they were due to arrive. Stories were told of savage treatment and despair was general. They packed their belongings, set off and left the oasis to the cultivators.

The tribes split up. Some migrated to Ayer and the lands of the blacks. Other families moved to Tunisia, Algeria and Timbuktu. Further fragments continued to wander around

Hamada which suffered from the oppressive heat of the sun and the rigours of the endless drought.

Tazidirat and her grandmother joined the fragments of the tribe that opted to stay in the open country of Hamada. Open country did not cover the whole of the barren Hamada area, but she well remembered those cruel skies, utterly cloudless. The savage sun was never veiled by a cloud all through those years. Drought and hunger were unremitting. Tazidirat lived with a whole generation that felt no rain and saw no cloud.

She never set eyes on running water, nor witnessed a flood herself.

She witnessed it only through the eyes of her grandmother. She used to sit by her round the waning fire at the entrance to the tent. The old woman would finish reciting her talismans. Tazidirat would clutch the ends of her black wrap and beg her to tell her about the floods. The old woman would not every time respond to her demands. She would often slip away, finding excuses. As a little girl Tazidirat was unaware of the pain these stories gave the old woman.

Once she saw her make a sudden move after telling her one of the stories of the floods. She sprinkled some water on the fire, putting it out. She hugged the tent pole and buried her head in her wrap and wept and wept. On another occasion she broke down while telling the story and was overcome by a long sobbing fit. Sometimes she would begin to cry as she told a story. But she gave up trying to conceal her tears as she had done before. And she told interesting tales about the great floods the desert had seen in olden days when the skies would pour down rain and the lands would flow with water for months on end. And all the time tears would quietly trickle down her pale bony cheeks without her wiping them away. But what interested Tazidirat most in the old woman's stories was that the flood *had* to sweep away a man, a woman or a child whenever it came. It did not surprise her that they lost animals that would take shelter in the wadi bed, but why did it have to seize human beings as well as beasts? She was baffled and asked her grandmother about it.

"It is because", the old woman replied, "the wretched people are mean in offering sacrifices and ignore the signs. They think they can deceive the heavens. The flood is obliged to exact its dues from them by force."

"Isn't it content with the souls of goats and of camels?" Tazidirat then asked. "Aren't animals sacrifices as well?"

The grandmother answered with words that remained in the mind of the granddaughter for the rest of her life.

"Animals are minor sacrifices. That is not enough for the flood. The flood is a hard task master and is satisfied only with the blood of man. If the flood wasn't hard it would not absent itself for tens of years and deprive us of what we need for half our lives."

Tazidirat had been deprived of the flood for all her life.

III

She could remember only two unfriendly elements in oasis life : the parched ground and the swirling dust.

She used to go to a copse of palm trees and bring back clover for the goats. The sun would be up and its burning rays would have scorched the sand. She had to come back on the fiery path with the green bundle on her head. Sometimes she crawled on her stomach like a snake with the load crushing her head. On other occasions she would roll over like a ball, dragging her bundle behind her on a piece of string. It was useless to complain to her grandmother. The old woman mumbled her charms and answered that patience in life was mightier than any magical talisman.

"It was not by chance that you were named Tazidirat," she told her, "for that means patience."

So instead of fortifying herself with the strongest talismans or questioning the holy man about her name she would go out and bring back huge bundles of clover and scatter them on the path to shield her feet from the scorching sand.

Her grandmother asked one of the cultivators to make her a pair of sandles from palm leaves. But they were useless. They were badly made. The binding on the right shoe wore away and it fell to pieces on the first day. She used the left shoe for both feet in turn until that too fell to pieces after a couple of days.

She learned that the scorched ground in the oasis was preordained and she could seek protection only through her mother's prescription : patience!

As for the dust it gave her frightful headaches and spells of nausea.

The oasis lay at a place called AI Tumas between the two deserts : the clayey desert of the north and the sandy desert of the south. Thick clouds of dust swirled up whenever the wind blew from the south. It veiled the sun and turned day into night. She remembered one dust storm that attacked for several days, forcing people to stay in their homes. It swept away huts and palm trees and buried cultivation and wells.

Such a storm brought on headaches and sickness.

Then they migrated to Hamada.

In the northern desert the weather as well as the nature of the land was different. The ground was not so hot and the dust storms were milder. But the sun was as unrelenting as ever and tyrannised over them with the utmost savagery.

During the first months she did not expose herself to the sun for long. Her grandmother gave her the job of collecting firewood and the sun itself assisted her in the task. For the plants had been parched and every green tree was turned into wood ready for the fire. But the longer they stayed in the wadis, the more firewood they used. She had to go further from the tents and bring firewood from the more distant wadis. She was alone with the sun and at times got very thirsty, but she always managed to retain consciousness enough to find her way back to the settlement.

Then she was entrusted with the goats and her grandmother told her to keep an eye on them as they grazed.

The goats! My God, what pests those goats were! She had often heard from the other girls about the cursedness of these creatures but never imagined that they would outdo the parched ground or the sun in their chastisement of human kind. In the first days Tamima, a relation, went with her to the ample pasturelands in the plains to the west.

Tamima was a happy lively girl two years older. She had spent all her life in Hamada. She had known the famine and had suffered from the sun. She had learned patience and acquired an immunity from the tyranny of the goats. Her mother plaited her hair into long slender braids tied at the back into an absurd bundle like a crown of thorns. She liked to fasten it with a cord made of palm fibres. Tamima went around the wadis, leaping on to rocks with the agility of the goats and... singing. She sang and sometimes danced and dreamed of the day she would be old enough to marry the proud young man, Akhnoukhan. She often hesitated about her choice. She kept on asking about other young men who might be more suitable as a bridegroom. One day she would name Akhnoukhan because he was proud and haughty. Then the next day she would forget about him and select Amud because she had noticed that he was even haughtier than Akhnoukhan and his head-dress was larger than Akhnoukhan's.

Meanwhile she never gave up dancing and singing as she pursued the wretched goats through wadis, plains, hills and mountain vales. She never suffered from fatigue. Nor was there every any sweat on her brow. But Tazidirat was a child of the oasis and was not schooled in wiles by the Hamada. Life had not given her the magic gift of patience, save in name. Weariness sapped her and her dress was soaked in sweat. Her throat was dry and she dawdled a long way behind her companion.

Tamima waved her lotus stick in the air and turned back laughing. As soon as she saw the distress in her friend's face she stopped and offered words to give her strength.

"These are goats. Pasturing goats is no simple matter, is it?"

She often said this to urge her on.

On one trip Tazidirat got bored and asked her companion.

"Why do the grown-ups give us the goats to look after when they know it's so tough."

They were lying down under an isolated lotus tree on the bare plain that was scattered with sharp rocks, blackened by the sun's rays. Tamima toyed with a twig from the white thorned sidr tree.

"The grown-ups do it deliberately," she said sagely, "so as to

get their own back on their own wretched childhood. They too had
to look after the goats when they were little," she laughed.

"That's not fair. The old men should take responsibility for
the goats. To look after goats, you need to be able to run things.
Old men have got the minds for that."

"Being able to run things is what makes them play this trick
on us. Because they can run things they say it's harder to look
after camels so they give the bloody goats to us kids to look after.
One day I,m going to hand them over to the wolves!"

"It's not fair. It would be fairer to let us take the sheep and
camels out to graze."

"Nothing's fair in this world. I told you that running things is
just a trick. My mum says a trick is a trick."

"It's better for grown-ups to bring up children. Can a child
bring up a child? A kid bring up a kid?"

"Tell that to your grandma," said Tamima with a smile.

Tamima pulled the cord tight round her waist. She crawled
round to catch some of the shade that was slipping away. Then she
said,

"Let's stop talking about goats. Let's talk about getting
married. Have you chosen your bridegroom?"

Tazidirat said sadly, the goats still on her mind.

"What's the use of getting married?"

"Is there anything in the world nicer than getting married?"

"You're stupid! The flood is much nicer."

Tamima lay down on her tummy, chin in one hand and the
other hand in the sand.

"The only thing in your head is rain and floods," she said.
"Woman was made to be a bride and man was made to be a
bridegroom. I don't know anything beyond that."

"So? What's the use of a man without the flood? What's the
use of the ground without rain? Only the flood can offset the sun
and destroy the three Evils."

"The three Evils?"

"Parched land, dust storms and thirst."

Tamima burst out laughing. "All you think about is parched
land and dust storms. The oasis pursues you even in Hamada."

"I've dreamt of the flood all my life. I've never ever seen a flood. Tell me about it."

"Not until you tell me about oasis weddings."

"Tell me first about the flood. I thought of the idea first, I swear in the name of all that's holy. In the name of Akhnoukhan."

"But I've only seen a flood in my dreams," Laughed Tamima.

There was silence. A great big fly came and settled on Tamima's bare leg. She chased it off with her other foot and listened to the silence. Some distant bleating came up from the wadi bed. She looked up at Tazidirat and saw sadness in her eyes as she gazed out at the emptiness with its mirages. Then she saw tears welling up in her eyes.

IV

It was midsummer and Tamima was sick with a fever. Tazidirat went out to do the grazing by herself. She went to the pasturelands of the wadis to the west. They were nearer and the wadi banks had plenty of shady trees. The sun became oppressive early and promised a day of infernal heat. Tazidirat congratulated herself on choosing this grazing area. But the fiendish goats would not let her enjoy the shade. As soon as she settled under a sidr tree or nestled her head among the leaves of a bush, preparing to take a rest and to nibble at a date she noticed that the wretched animals had rushed off into the wadi out of sight. She put the date back in her bag and set off after them. She often used to resort to a ruse Tamima had taught her. She would cross the wadi with its many branches and head across open country to shorten the distance and then cut the goats off at a bend. But Tamima had warned her not to play this trick too often because wolves would take the chance to intercept the goats before she did.

Tazidirat's heart pounded as soon as she recalled the wolves and the speed with which these wild creature could kill off their prey. She could not see any wolves and did not even hear a howl. But tribal lore and the words of the wise spoke only of the fearlessness of this enemy. She could imagine this wild evil creature alone with a herd of miserable goats separated from her, tearing at the throats of the goats with its frightful fangs - as happened in the fairy stories.

She chose not to go across country but to follow them.

Whenever she caught up with the herd she saw that one goat was in the lead and drawing behind it all the others. This goat was less than one month old. A neighbouring woman had forcibly fed it. It had been deprived not only of a mother's milk but also of a mother, who had been tethered to a peg at the tent's entrance. The kid was not allowed to go near her. The neighbour said she wanted to keep the milk for her sick son who was suffering from loss of appetite, After the goats were separated they would not let anyone in all the nearby tents get any sleep. The mother goat was tied up by the rest of the herd and the kid would raise up a din with its bleating and complaining. Its mother would reply. Their bleatings were like point and counterpoint. First the kid howled and then the mother from the opposite direction. The kid's endless bleating brought on the anger of the billy goats and especially one young male who would butt it fiercely to make it shut up. Tazidirat's grandmother often woke up to the noise of this corrective action and Tazidirat would hear her mumbling in the dark.

This kid was in front. Whenever she caught up with it and blocked its way it would stop and stare at her defiantly with ill-tempered eyes that were almost human. It would then lower its head and paw the ground with its front hoof nervously and repeatedly, as if about to charge her. It would then realise that it did not have any horns yet and would cry out in a high-pitched voice, cocking its head back and up. It would then leap to one side and dash off vaulting over the rocks like a gazelle... or like a mythical beast of ill omen.

At first its behaviour made her laugh. She laughed even though she was also tired and angry. The kid was always in front of the others. But when that dark evil angry glare was directed at her again and again a sense of undefined dread and terror crept over her as if this rogue was not a young goat but was a creature possessed by some evil human being. It was not its hostility or its precocious desire to butt her that were the cause of these feelings. It was that eerie diabolical ferocious look. Its eyes were not as the eyes of other goats which expressed emotions apart from anger and hatred.

Then she herself began to feel anger and hatred. This was because she had not been able to eat her date or to drink the water from her waterskin or to lie down in the shade and enjoy herself. She cursed the kid, she cursed the sun, she cursed the oases and she cursed herself. She cursed herself because, unlike Tamima, she could not control the goats in spite of all the time she had spent in Hamada.

She tried to hold back her anger but the tears poured out. She picked up a stone and ran after them. She overtook the lagging animals and went on running. They went round the wadi and turned off to the right. She kept to the left side and ran along the edge of the wadi bed. Finally she caught up with the evil kid who pranced around in the air as if demented, not permitting the others a chance to rest or to graze. Goats never turn aside to herbage or to a tree however hungry they are, if a frolicsome kid is among them. This malign goat would not rest until it had handed the herd over to the wolves. There are legends that tell us that.

She stood facing it, drenched with sweat. Her throat was dry. Her mouth also. She took a couple of steps forward. It threatened her with its ferocious eyes. It lowered its head, but its right hoof did not stir. She raised her hand and threw a stone at its head, screaming words of hatred at it. But the crazed goat did not move. It did not appear to be hurt by the blow. It looked up at her with its sullen eyes. The passive expression was both clear and obscure. What did it threaten? She felt an indefinable terror, a terror like that caused by the hiss of a snake.

She stepped back and collapsed helplessly beneath a tree. She wanted the wolves to come and pick it off and deal with it. She added that kid to her three Evils and execrated it in her heart.

She drank thirstily from her waterskin. The water trickled on to her chest and she recalled the flood. There were tears on her cheeks.

V

On the other side of the wadi bed a hill rose up that was in the shape of a camel's hump. The sun poured over it a ration of fire which hovered and then flowed down the slopes to burn the bushes and crack the rocks and soak the desert with mirages and fire.

The afternoon rest.

She settled down in the shade of a bush and was unaware of sleep stealing over her. She only dozed for a few minutes but she had a dream. In it she saw a crowd of women dressed in black gathering in the desert and walking out until they were swallowed up by the horizon. She felt anxious and then Tamima came along, laughing, and told her that the women were burying that evil young goat. She looked up to offer her thanks to Heaven, Tamima pinched her botton and she shuddered. She woke up from her doze and scratched her bottom. She went on feeling anxious. It was the same sense of foreboding she felt when she saw the women gathering in the desert.

Then she remembered the goats.

VI

She lost the tracks of the goats at the end of Hamada. The endless emptiness stretched on to the merciless lands of the west. The wadis and their branches led up to the bare grey mountains where they disappeared into openings that were wild and dark.

She stood on the top of a hill and saw below her in a deep valley a hawk stretch out its sturdy wings and glide in a circle that was confined by the grim mountains. The rays of the declining sun glinted on its wings from time to time and its feathers flashed with a weird glow.

She sat on the sun-blackened rocks and drank from the waterskin. She felt dazed and calm. She gazed at the sun, a purple orb hanging over the horizon at the end of the lower wadis. From her lofty perch she saw thirsty bushes scattered about the wadis.

144

Their pathetic wretchedness was heartbreaking. Even so, beneath the purple rays of the sunset she was aware of a pleasantly sad beauty.

She recalled the legends of the tribe about the transformation of this hard grey land when the heavens took pity and blessed the desert with floods. A myriad of plants broke up the land and cracked open the rocks. The desert became green in a few days. The desolate wadis became covered with shrubs, and charming flowers opened up to give off a fragrance that was so strong that it made the herdsmen dizzy. Her grandmother spoke of spring in Hamada as a lost paradise from which God excluded the people of the desert as a punishment for their misdeeds. When she came to talk about the truffles her eyes would cloud over and she would sway to left and to right as if in a trance. She would tell of other desert herbs too but she was in a state of ecstasy at mention of the blessed truffle fruit.

She used to weave fictions about the black plant - its legendary form, size, colour, smell and taste. Tazidirat had so frequently heard these tales that she began to share the old woman's rapture. She too swayed to right and to left at the end of each tale. She was distressed that she had not been born at the time of the floods and sobbed into her bedclothes in secret, grieving for the lost Paradise.

Her unhappy star had been pleased to let her be born during years of drought and famine, years of the sun's oppression, years of invasions. Her yearning for the flood unconsciously became an obsession. Her lost Paradise, her one object of desire. The girls boasted of the day when they would be brides to young men crowned with blue turbans and sitting on thrones of sand. And here she was lusting for a day when the sky would be clouded over, when the merciless sun would be in shade, when the tears of anger and compassion would be shed on to the northern heights to drown the desert with a flood that would wash the world away. Whenever she expressed her hopes to Tamima, her friend would laugh and tell her she was crazy. For her only men merited adoration. Tamima had been lucky. When she had lived in the oases she had enjoyed seeing some passing rain bearing clouds. And one year she saw the full trickle of a stream. She claimed that this had happened twice but Tazidirat was not sure whether to believe her. But this thin skein of water had helped to quench her thirst. She no longer thirsted like Tazidirat for the flood but only for men.

The purple orb of the sun sank and was swallowed up by the horizon. But the heat continued to come up out of the ground and the roasted stones began to give off steam. The lone kite still hovered in the gloom of the ravine. Tazidirat sat on the grey rocks of this wild deserted perch. She looked down on the wadi beds in sad silence. As darkness fell she seemed to be like a young jinn dreaming of Paradise. Then she remembered about the missing goats.

VII

Then she made a vow, not from fear of death but from a craving, an anxiety, a primitive yearning for the flood she had never seen.

Thirst restored her to consciousness.

Her water ran out so she folded the waterskin into a pillow and rested on it in the narrow valley on her way back. Although she was tired she was able to doze off only towards dawn. She heard the wolves howl and the jinns whisper. She saw ghosts fumbling around out there beneath the pale moonlight. She saw the solitary hawk swooping down in a vertical attack on some poor goat in the dark ravine.

She woke up and dropped off a score of times before the tyrant sun swamped the desert with its tongues of fire. She carried on walking trying to find her way back to the settlement. The mountainous terrain with its scattered grey rocks left no trace of her tracks : they were obliterated as had the tracks of the goats been lost. The ruthless sun edged its way up over the horizon. She marched towards it with firm steps as if she were challenging it, advancing with intent to cut off its head and to put an end to her suffering and its desire to humiliate. It was the law of the desert that all who lost their way were obliged to surrender their fate to the all powerful sun, which offered relief at will and abducted at will. Many were saved but many went astray for ever and not even the strongest of these were seen again. She wandered towards the fierce sun until noon... until the hour of the afternoon rest. Her uncovered head was burnt and her brain felt as if it was boiling over. The sun was seated on its throne on high and she was lost.

She stumbled. She fell down and got up again. This happened again and again. She was in the lethal grip of the sun which tightened on her in response to her defiance.It lobbed a cloud into her face which blocked her vision. Not long after that another cloud dulled her mind. She knelt down and tore off the amulet that had been tied round her neck. It was made from three pieces of leather formed into a triangle. She looked for the pin that held it together. Her grandmother had hung it on her neck before the child knew what life was all about, what it had to offer or what death was. She had told her that she had bought it from an oasis sage, paying three goats. The first of the three parts helped to appease the jinns. The second was designed to frustrate the wiles of mankind. And the third was to keep the mind from disorder, a complaint that was common in the desert. For it affected neighbouring tribes and threatened to turn the best of men and the fairest of women into beings possessed.

Fear of such a fate made the old woman keen to have this valuable charm and she had paid the sage three whole goats for the three-part charm, though one goat would have paid for the other two parts by themselves.

Tazidirat found the pin and took it in her trembling fingers. She pricked her arm violently and repeatedly. She bent over and sucked the blood. She felt no pain when she stabbed herself just as she did not feel the liquid welling from her arm. She collapsed panting. Then she sat up again and stabbed her right knee. She bent down and sucked at her knee. There was no taste. Perhaps the blood left the body in the same way that water evaporated in the blazing sun. She took the pin away and buried her head in the sand. She chewed at the hot sand and pebbles but that too had no taste. Suddenly her head cleared up. In this fleeting instant she made her momentous pledge. Then she had another blackout. She surrendered to this oblivion.

VIII

They came upon her fast asleep in the afternoon.

She was in a coma for three days. She groaned, mumbled and came out with gibberish that was without meaning to her grandmother who stayed up all night with her, reciting charms and muttering the kursi verse from the Qurán. She boiled unguents and herbs and churned milk at daybreak. Old women show most compassion for the young when they ail. She took the opportunity to pamper her.

On the morning of the third day Tazidirat showed her face.

"Why did God make the desert?", she asked.

The old woman carried on swinging the goatskin of milk to left and to right. She looked at her and smiled before answering.

"So as to offer a place to escape to for anyone who wants to be free."

Tazidirat smiled back. She looked at the fire in the brazier and then at the old woman's skinny face and hollow cheeks. After a moment's silence she asked,

"Are city people slaves?"

"Of course they are," came the answer without hesitation.

"And the oasis people?"

The old woman nodded and explained.

"Yes, they are slaves too. Anybody who is content to live at the mercy of a slave is himself a slave. Anybody who sleeps under a roof or lives behind walls, anybody who settles down in the world."

"What about jungle people? Are they slaves too?"

She nodded.

"But," objected Tazidirat, "they don't live under roofs or behind walls."

"They live in the shadow of fear. How can you go to sleep trembling with anxiety about wolves and about snakes and yet be free?"

"But in the desert people also die from the drought."

"They die, aware of it. There is no escape from death, even when a man wishes to be free."

"But what's the point of freedom in the desert if it is decreed that man must die?"

"What's the point of a life in chains?"

She went on swinging the skin to and fro in rhythm. Her cheeks became paler and hollower. On her lips played the traces of a sad smile.

That evening Tamima came to visit her and asked about the goats.Her merry eyes gazed long at her face. Then she bent over and said,

"What are you worried about? They are not all lost. The wolves had destroyed only half of them when the herdsmen caught up with them."

She then glanced at her with embarrassment and said in a tome full of import,

"The baby next door that was sick has also died."

IX

The girls grew up.

The young bloods of the tribe were not slow to woo them. Tamima of course was first in the race and was first to wed.

She won the second contest too and soon gave birth to three sons. She came often to call on Tazidirat and tell her all about the married state. She dragged her children along and swung the youngest around in the air and then swept him up with all the skill of a true mother and said,

"I don't have any regrets, unlike others. I still maintain that life consists of Men. The woman who has not tasted a man has not lived. I shall not rest content until I see you in the arms of the best of them. The tribe is not short of champions."

Tazidirat provoked her with her old jest.

"Not before the desert is flooded."

Once Tamima got fed up with the joke and snapped at her,

"The flood... the flood. And if the desert is not flooded? Will you fritter your life away waiting for the unknown?"

They were sitting in the evening shade. Tamima stirred some

green tea. She took a sip to see how sweet it was and added, in the tone of a wise old woman,

"Women are like flowers. They open up quickly and then fade away at the same speed. But men are ageless. That is their good fortune. A man is always in the bloom of youth. God, how I envy them."

She then turned on Tazidirat,

"And here are you waiting for the flood. You'll fade away before it comes."

"It'll come, you'll see. I won't enjoy men. I won't enjoy anything."

"God help you," murmured Tamima, "a girl who refuses marriage is denying God's blessed gift. How many have made an approach so far?"

She did not wait for a reply but counted on her fingers.

"Seven," she concluded. "Seven just from our tribe. My mum says they wanted to marry you off to somebody from a distant tribe. From the Aifughas."

"I refused them all as well," she said, chuckling to herself.

Tamima frowned crossly and leant over the tea pot.

The grandmother returned after calling on another old woman in the neighbourhood. She came in with a lively step even though back had bent double in recent years. Her pale cheeks were even bonier. She came in tugging her black shawl against the gusts of wind from the north. She settled down by Tamima and joined in on her side. Tamima handed her a cup of bubbly tea. She sipped at the coloured cup and said,

"May your cause win, my dear. Tell her, by God, that you don't live to the age of Noah in our tribe. My wish is to see her children before I die. Don't I have the right to enjoy my grand-daughter's child like any other old woman? You are young. You don't realise that the best of children is a grandson. How happy an old woman is who lives to dandle the son of her grandson in her arms!"

She sighed and sipped her tea.

"Tazidirat is not being fair to me in this. She wants to deprive me. I'm tired. Help me, Tamima. Look after me, for God's sake."

Tazidirat stirred and changed the subject. She did not encourage their interest in marriage but talked of the desert instead.

"Grandma keeps saying that everybody who lives under a roof or settles down is a slave," she told her friend. "You say there's no freedom outside the desert. Freedom only exists for the traveller in God's vast desert. Have you ever heard a view like her's before?"

At that moment she thought of something else. She kept to herself an idea that had always explained to herself the concept of savage justice. "Freedom is the desert. The desert means drought. Death. Freedom then is death. "Whenever she pondered this inwardly she thought of the flood that was to be expected, she became overcome with a frenzy of trembling. In time that inner reflection became like her momentous pledge. Her secret.

X

When she was unable to persuade her to accept a son of their tribe the old woman commended to her the young bloods of other tribes. She did not describe the Aifughas as strangers and pointed out that her mother was a Fughasi and so they were cousins on the maternal side. Any girl who won such a cousin would be happy in marriage. When she observed Tazidirat losing interest she would tell her gripping tales of heroes and quests undertaken by horsemen from afar. On nights of full moon they went outside and sat before the tent by the animal pen. She would dig her hands and feet in the cold sand and embark on her tales of heroes. There existed no tribe throughout the length and breadth of the great desert but she found for their brave young men a famous battle that merited a hymn of praise. Here she would throw in a verse and there a sad song until Tazidirat was enthralled. She would never have guessed for a moment that her grandmother had so many verses off by heart. The grandmother would end the story by saying that she had received news from one of the fine spirits of the tribe who had come to seek the hand of Tazidirat for his brave son. Sometimes she would forget that she had told the same circumstantial tales about other tribal suitors. They would develop into legends of the purest fantasy that she had told her when she was a little girl. Many a time Tazidirat had to smother her giggles and turn them cheekily into a fit of coughing. The old woman made a wry face and stopped, only to resume the assault the following day.

One night Tazidirat lost control and burst into derisive laughter at some slip the old woman made. The mockery brought on a terrible reaction. Her grandmother suddenly went very quiet. She turned away and looked up at the clouds. She took her hands out of the cold sand. She pulled her black shawl over her face and appeared in the darkness of the new moon like some fearsome spectre. She said in a voice that seemed to come from the depth of a well, "I wanted to see..." but did not complete the sentence. Her tiny bunched up body seemed in the open air to be very frail. Tazidirat said savagely, "And I wanted to see the flood. You've got to tell me about the flood."

She did not know why she spoke so savagely. The old woman stopped telling tales of heroes. She went off to call on the wise old woman. Her visits then stopped and she went to a small hillock in the open country south of the settlement. The children called it 'The Dervish's Bald Pate!' Nobody knew how far it resembled the bald pate of a dervish. nor had anyone any idea how far it differed from the bald pate of other wise men of the tribe.

People found themselves adopting the name. The old woman found herself spending several nights on the hillock after the wise old woman had disappointed her by not coming up with anything that indicated that relief from disaster was at hand.

The grandmother managed to steal away several times before Tazidirat became aware that she was missing. One night she went out to answer a call of nature and saw a skinny bent form groping about in the desert. She thought it was one of the ghosts of Jabal Nasawana. She turned away and recited the kursi verse from the Qur'an, but it did not go away. Indeed it slowly and mockingly came towards her. She stopped, expecting it to cuff her or to spit on her or to make some other gesture of unfriendliness. But it carried on regardless, went right past her and into the tent. She went herself back into the tent and saw it waiting for her there. In the darkness she then realised that it was her grandmother. She asked her why she was roaming about the haunted desert at that time of night but the grandmother made no reply. She heard her muttering her charms and get under her black shawl in a corner of the tent near the waterskin.

The next night she kept close to her, following her tracks. She saw the poor old woman rubbing herself up against an old circular tomb with an opening a few feet off the ground. Tazidirat squatted on the slope and watched her grandmother resting her head on the tomb and dozing off. She was amazed that she had been unaware of the existence of this tomb on the Dervish's Bald Pate before she caught her grandmother on it, apparently practising some rite. She forgot that desert people do not set up camp unless they are near such a tomb. They say that people who do not live near the tombs of holy men are blind. They do not observe the wiles of fate and they expose their lives to great danger.

In the morning Tazidirat went to see a black neighbour about this practice.

"I used to think that tombs like this were just the resting place of one who is no more," she told her.

The wise negress laughed, displaying a toothless mouth.

"Is there anything that is no more," she said, "like rain that is no more?"

"Can the tomb foretell the flood?"

"Who else can foretell the flood?"

She then made some tea and told her she should offer her body to a man before that body withered and became flabby and eaten away. She told her that God had bestowed beauty on women not to keep for themselves but to give to a man. When she saw that Tazidirat was irritated by this, she said consolingly,

"The flood will come. Where can it fly to? Do you imagine that you are alone in being obsessed by it? The desert has a greater yearning for it than you. Its soil pants for it. It suffers from its absence more than you. Have patience. Where can it fly to?"

A few days later the grandmother asked her,

"Will you select a groom when the rains bring a flood?"
Her heart fluttered. She could hear it beating. She recalled
her pledge. She recalled her savage compact and whispered.
"I will."
The old woman sighed deeply.
"It has been my dream to hear these words before I die."
Was it strange that she died a few days later? Nobody knows
better than the old women of the desert what fate has in store.

XI

Rqq... rqq... rqq... lqq... lqq... lqq...
She preferred copying the latter sound. It was nearer the
language of water, closer to its mysterious dialogue with the stones
and the tree. How sweet this babbling was. How sweet this water
was.
She paddled in the stream, upstream, barefoot. She stopped to
listen. She imitated the enigmatic sound. She examined this flood
that was so strange. She bent down and tried to work out what
colour it was, to smell it, to savour its taste. There was no colour,
no smell, no taste. And yet it had the power to temper the tyranny
of the sun and to give fresh life to land that had been dead for a
thousand years. It was like nothing and it was everything. It was
the simplest of things yet it was life itself. What is life without
running water?
She enjoyed it fondling her feet. She chuckled at the strength
of the caresses. She tried to read its secret in its complex language.
The mystery became deeper and deeper. Her heart became fonder
and fonder.
The wadi divided the settlement in two. People gathered on
both sides. The crowds increased and voices rose and people called
to each other. Then, like a clap of thunder, there burst from the
women the sound of heartfelt trilling. There followed cries of
children and bleating of goats.
Cold gusts blew from the north. A breeze drenched in rain.
She opened her heart to it and tasted it. She looked up and beheld

another miracle. The sun had been extinguished. It was veiled behind thick clouds that moved slowly and majestically, floating to the south. And then. And then. The horizon was lit up with threads of fire. They appeared in the twinkling of an eye and were snuffed out as soon as they appeared. This was lightning. But she did not hear the explosion of thunder. It was said that flashes of lightning were always connected with crashes of thunder. She remembered another of her grandmother's sayings, "If you see lightning and do not hear thunder, then that really is a good sign." She did not hear the thunder. Nor did she hear somebody shouting at her.

"Hey you! Hey you! Get out of the wadi. The water is rising. The flood is coming. Mind the flood."

She laughed. Her heart was beating, full of joy. Was this indeed happiness? She knelt down in the water. The charmed liquid played with her knees, dug under them and covered them with sand. It got under her dress. It nibbled at her right thigh. Then it stretched out to reach her left thigh. She laughed and leant over to listen to the sound it made as it rushed down. She felt the water on her soft lips that had suffered from thirst for a thousand years. She permitted the naughty water to play with her lips and to caress them with a kiss that lingered and lingered. She bore the desires of a thousand years. She then took her lips away and felt dizzy. She opened her eyes and tears tumbled down into the water. Her heart overflowed with another gust of joyousness. Fresh tears trickled from her eyes.

The level of the water rose.

The current became stronger, more impetuous. The water got muddy. It dragged along tufts of grass, animal droppings and mud. She clutched at the bank but the water dug beneath her and cunningly pulled at her. It coiled round her to include her in its embrace. It was now up to her waist.

She bent down to drink. She took a long draft. The water was muddy. She stood upright. She spat out mud and goat droppings. Her thirst was unappeased but raged furiously. A nameless fire flared up, charming her inside with the severest thirst. She bent over again and drank avidly.

She vomited again - a mixture of dung, mud and bits of

grass.

The water wrestled with her, trying to bring her to the ground. She held on to a bush. She got her balance back and stood up. The flood sapped away at the soil once again trying to bring her to the ground. She laughed and sank back on to her knees. Her heart was ablaze with joy and thirst.

She began to take her clothes off.

She was first free of her shawl. The current snatched it from her hand and swept it away. The water seemed to be getting wilder and more violent. She tore at her flowing dress. She ripped off the upper part around the throat, tearing it into two large pieces. She got rid of the right hand piece. The flood was taking her over and swallowing her up now. She continued as she sank in the swirling water to feed it with the rest of her dress and stood there completely naked. Now and then she caught hold of the bush to maintain her balance. Thunder rumbled. She heard it clearly. A rumble of promise, terrible to hear, drowning the noise of the flood.

She knelt down and was hugged by the water, It was ravishing her naked virgin body, sweeping it along in its love, She tossed her head back. The water reached her neck and flooded over her tresses. Her grip weakened and she lost hold of the bush. The flood embraced her and took her away. It felt light as a bird's plumage. The water was soothing as it tenderly embraced her virgin body. She gave herself up and glided along with the noisy current as it rushed down sweeping away tufts of grass and lumps of dung. The flood ploughed up the untouched land with the fury of a demonic lover who flees with his fair sweetheart off to unknown lands.

Mohammed Salmawy
A CONCERTO
FOR THE NAY

Translated by Amira el-Maghrabi

The *nay*, pronounced 'nigh', is an oriental reed
flute made of bamboo and without a mouthpiece.
It is usually held in a slanting forward position

His earliest recollections were those of being dug deep in the black
mud on the banks of the Nile in Upper Egypt where the bamboo
grows in thick, dense groves. From the very start this stalk was
strikingly more beautiful than the rest.

The first three months, still green, he stood a supple, slender
stem, his nodes perfectly chiselled, until the sweltering rays of
Upper Egypt's blazing sun transformed him into a smooth, shiny
golden stalk. He became the centre of attraction. The migrating
birds, before starting their long northward journey, would flutter
back to take a last glimpse of that smooth, shiny surface. The fish
and all the other river creatures would swim close, or at times
fling themselves out of the water to rest at the foot of his stem and
in one last look take in all his beauty and perfection before they
died. But he attached little or no importance to all this, for he was
certain that he had been created for another life, something far
better than the primitive country existence surrounding him. He
was forever dreaming of going to Cairo like some of his higher-
standing peers, the ones known as Indian Bamboo, which were
cultivated with exceeding care in special plantations and were

transferred to the city where they were made into fishing poles, or other peers, the ones with thick stems, which were made into furniture and decorative objects.

His ambitions, however, soared far higher. He was not going to accept being transformed into a commonplace fishing pole, swaying in the hands of a white-hatted old man sitting on a beach in Alexandria. Nor was he going to be debased into a chair for some ignorant human being to rest on. He would refuse that fate as much as he refused his present situation under the burning summer sun, and the slashing winter winds and rain. That was not what this perfect stem had been created for.

He was intuitively aware that one day, very soon, he would be entrusted to the hands of one of the best makers of musical instruments in Cairo, where he would be made into a unique *nay*, a *nay* of a quality hitherto unheard of, a *nay* that would fill the air with such heart-rending sounds that people would stop to listen. There would be a black oblong box with red velvet, or green felt lining, wherein he would be treasured for a grand occasion. From among thousands of others it was he who would be chosen for the first oriental concerto to be composed for the *nay*.

He dreamed of a gala performance at the Opera House, attended by official dignitaries, men of letters, artists and the cream of high society. Peoples' eyes would be riveted not on the symphony orchestra, nor on the visiting European conductor's baton, but on that exquisite *nay* and the music emanating from it. As for the experts in symphonic music, they would soon discover that he was in no way different from the rest of the western wind instruments, be it the clarinet, flute, oboe or bassoon.

Whenever he looked at the surrounding environment, the black mud at his feet, small river creatures, ugly snails and algae, he felt nauseated. He had once heard from a foreign scientist visiting the area to take some samples of the soil, that there existed over thirty million different varieties of microscopic organism, bacteria, amoeba etc, in every one gram of soil. If that was the case, then how could he, who was about to become a *nay*, live in such a polluted environment?

He spoke to no one, and he listened to no one, for the sounds that drifted over to him were all discords. They were sounds made by the rustling of bamboo stalks against one another, or the sounds of frogs and crickets in the evening. Sounds he could not bear to hear and that kept him awake at night. Instead he would only hear the sounds of his inner consciousness. They were not the insipid folk songs sung by the local people, but the sublime music composed in the form of a grand concerto for the *nay*.

No composer had actually written that concerto yet, but he already knew it by heart. There would be a lengthy overture to enhance and heighten his introduction, for after such a long delay in collaborating with the Symphony Orchestra, the *nay* could not possibly be introduced after the first few bars like the poor violin in Sibelius' or Mendelssohn's concertos.

Moreover, his introduction would come as an unexpected surprise, for everyone would be waiting to hear oriental melodies, those usually played on the *nay*, but his music would be purely Western and gradually the audience would forget that they were listening to an Egyptian concerto composed for an Oriental instrument. As they became captivated by the beauty of his music, they would think they were listening to Beethoven's Emperor concerto, or one of Bach's Brandenburg concertos.

He knew the details of the three movements of this unprecedented symphonic opus. The first movement would be an *allegro can brio*, the second an *andante maestoso* and the finale an *allegro molto vivace*.

Nor was this all, for his concerto was going to be totally different from all other concertos. It would not be the vague compositions Chopin wrote for his piano concertos where the piano and orchestra practically melt into one another. These reminded him of the melodies he had often heard from the village people when they passed by him, in their small boats playing monotonous tunes on their local *nays* - oh how it had bored him! His concerto would be different. He would not repeat any of the themes after the orchestra. Instead it was going to be the orchestra that would repeat after him. He would always be the originator at the forefront with the orchestra following his lead. He could not envisage the concerto as a harmonious well-arranged whole, but rather as a duel escalating into a conflict between his boundless, impetuous melodies, and the orchestra's vain attempts to catch up with him.

Finally, the expected day arrived. A group of barefoot *fellahin* staged an attack on the bamboo grove. They tore the bamboo stalks out from the ground, ripping out the dry foliage around them. It was known as the 'elimination process', usually completed at the beginning of the spring before the start of the *khamasin* winds. It was a painful and savage operation which he bore stoically. He could only think of the future that lay ahead of him in Cairo. He could hear the shrieks of pain emitted from the stalks around him as they were ripped by their roots from the earth. But *his* scream was more like the deep gasp of a newborn child before the first cry. A gasp that would be followed, in his case, not by a cry but by a passionate tune so powerful that after the gala evening at the Opera, people would not cease humming it after him.

He left for Cairo in a large truck that must have been sent especially for him, even though it carried hundreds of other things that he knew nothing about, for he hardly looked around him throughout the long trip from Upper Egypt to Cairo. He tried to endure the tiresome journey heroically but he could not. It was stiflingly crowded inside the truck. He missed the fresh air he had been used to, and the water too. He gradually began to feel the oppressive heat and the drought, then he fainted.

He awoke to find himself in a flat in Cairo. He had been dug into the soil of a large ornamental plant box. He was supporting a giant stalk of *ficus decora* that was beginning to lean backwards. He could not imagine how he had ended up in this place! There must have been some mistake. Where was the *nay* craftsman who ought to have been expecting him? Where was the concerto and the opening night at the Opera? He began to scream, but no one answered him for there was no one around except that dumb *ficus* plant. Everything surrounding him was artificial. The air was cold and dry, blowing from an electrical unit on the wall facing him. It was not the gentle breeze he knew, that blew on the banks of the Nile. The soil he had been dug into, as he later came to know, was peat moss imported from Ireland. It was not that natural soil he grew up in, but a compost of dry leaves, branches, other organic material and chemical additives. It was capable of absorbing water for longer periods than natural soil, thereby remaining moist, and it was completely free of insects, worms and all other types of organisms. As for the music he sometimes heard when there was a dinner party in the house, it was a music that was very strange to him, played by electronic instruments he had never heard before, and emanating from another electrical unit into which the hostess popped a cassette at regular intervals.

He decided to be a little more patient. Perhaps this was but a temporary phase after which he would reach the talented craftsman he had known in his dreams. But days passed by and turned into months, then into years, and he was still dug into his artificial soil in the plant box in that elegant flat in Cairo where no one paid him the least attention. He began to worry, then his worry soon turned into real fear when he realised that his dream was not coming true. He then felt that the end was nearing for rot was setting in at the base of his lower nodes that dug deep into the moist lifeless moss.

For the first time he began to feel a homesickness for his previous life on the Nile banks in Upper Egypt where there was the sunshine and the natural breeze; where autumn became winter, and spring turned into summer; where there was the companionship of the local bamboo stalks and the birds, the fish and the river snails, that had once surrounded him with warmth and comfort. He was now nostalgic for the sad strains of the *nay* that floated from passing boats on the Nile, and for the croaking frogs that formed a rhythmical background for that pure unadulterated melody. But what he missed above all was the black soil of the Nile, that bed of earth that had for thousands of years been the burial ground of ancestors, whether humans, animals or plants, and for everything that lived upon it enriching it, and making it the most fertile of all soils; that black earth of the Nile that had seen the first gleams of civilisation, that black earth that he would never see again, for once he left that elegant flat in Cairo he would be thrown away as trash.

Passport 4:
CHILDREN OF THE
REVOLUTION

Phillip Ramey
PAUL BOWLES:
A TIME OF FRIENDSHIP

Early in 1969, at a modern music concert in New York, Aaron Copland introduced me to a handsome, elegantly-dressed gentleman with grey hair. 'This,' he announced, looking as satisfied as an owl that has caught an especially succulent mouse, 'is Paul Bowles.'

A few months before, Aaron had recommended Bowles's short stories and novels and lent me a couple of volumes. I read them with growing fascination, for they seemed unlike anything else. It was not long before I was familiar with almost everything Bowles had written.

Bowles at one time had studied music composition with Copland. The two were old friends. I knew that Bowles lived in far-off Tangier. Aaron used to say, in wonderment: 'Paul and I went to Morocco in 1931, and he's still there.' Thus I was startled suddenly to find myself face to face with my new favourite author. With the enthusiasm of youth, I declared: 'I'm happy to meet you, Mr Bowles, because I've read your books and think they're original and wonderful.' The great man smiled coolly, took a languid puff from his cigarette-holder, and replied: 'Ah, yes?' Not having seen each other in some time, he and Aaron began a lengthy conversation. Twice I dared to interject a comment; twice Bowles looked my way but said nothing. Later, in a snit at being excluded, I complained to Aaron: 'Well, Paul Bowles certainly did not find *me* of any interest.' Aaron, amused, said soothingly: 'Don't be upset. Paul's always been something of a cold fish.'

When, thirteen years later in 1982, I decided to vacation in Morocco, Copland suggested visiting Bowles in Tangier, and a colleague who was to accompany me expressed enthusiasm for the idea. I was reluctant, remembering my less-than-gratifying encounter with the expatriate writer and composer. I reasoned that if Bowles, who had the reputation of being a recluse, was fond of visitors - in our case, unexpected visitors - he would hardly have isolated himself for decades in Morocco without a telephone. So when, after enjoying the sights of Marrakesh, Fez and Meknes, we arrived in Tangier, I had pretty much determined to forgo seeing him. Our room, high in the Rembrandt Hotel, had an impressive view of the harbour and the Strait of Gibraltar; there was another medina to explore, another casbah to investigate and more Arab coffee-houses in which to drink mint tea. It was *safi*, enough. Why ruin our stay by invading a stranger's privacy and being made to feel unwelcome? 'Look, I don't think this is a good idea - it's too pushy,' I said. 'Let's leave Mr Paul Bowles to his splendid isolation.' My colleague, a diminutive, rather humourless fellow who tended to be pleased with himself and found it difficult to imagine he might not be welcome everywhere, wasn't having that. 'We're going,' he snapped. 'I have the address, and we're going.'

Fortunately (or, I thought at the time, unfortunately), the taxi-driver knew the location of Immeuble Itesa, as Bowles's Führer-bunkeresque apartment building is called. The door to his flat was opened by a compact Moroccan, with a villainously friendly smile, who introduced himself as Mohammed Mrabet and retreated into the kitchen to brew tea. I recognised the name - Mrabet was one of several native writers whose works Bowles had translated into English - and I said to myself, ye gods, what a place: even the famous author's houseboy writes books!

In his dark, cavelike *sala*, the man whom the *Boston Globe* designated 'a literary god' sat on a floor cushion, contentedly smoking from his holder. My colleague and I introduced ourselves, and Bowles politely directed us to other cushions. Mrabet appeared with cups of tea and then began to puff at his *sebsi*. After some desultory conversation, silence fell. It occurred to me that I had travelled several thousand miles and tracked Bowles to his lair only to receive a further dose of indifference. As I began to plan revenge on my colleague, I heard him proclaim to Bowles that we were musicians, and that we brought greetings not only from Copland but from another friend, the composer-critic Virgil Thomson. At once Bowles's interest was engaged, and the ice melted. He had assumed. I think, that we were the usual book-fans, come to offer platitudes about his best-known novel, *The Sheltering Sky*; we would have our tea and depart, and he would breathe a sigh of relief. Music, however, was another matter.

During the next few days we visited Bowles regularly and discovered that he was always ready to discuss music and musicians. With his permission, we rummaged through his manuscripts, and he gave to my colleague, who was at that time a pianist, an unpublished piece; and to me a record of himself reading some of his stories, along with a note for Copland.

I didn't expect to see Morocco or Bowles again. But he and I exchanged a few letters, and when planning a trip to Lisbon two years later I couldn't resist a cheap air-fair to Tangier. So, I found myself once more at his door, this time not at all apprehensive and free of that tiresome if useful colleague. Bowles didn't seem displeased to see me. I had brought tapes of musical works with which he was unfamiliar, having been cut off to a great degree from Western concert music since removing himself to Morocco in 1947. I was amazed that he did not know, for instance, Copland's classic *Appalachian Spring* - which he termed 'one of the most beautiful pieces I've ever heard, but twice too long' (Copland's laughing retort when I told him was: 'Too late now!'). Nor was he really familiar with the *Short Symphony* - 'Aaron was working on that here, in Tangier, on our out-of-tune piano up on the Mountain, but I never heard an orchestra play it.' Or several late pieces by Stravinsky, who is perhaps his favourite composer. The list went on, and it was great fun - and instructive as well - to introduce him to all sorts of scores by major and minor composers and observe his reactions.

During the past several years, drawn by an agreeable climate, the possibility of piece and quiet for work and an evolving friendship with Bowles ('Make many more trips to T.,' he commanded in a 1985 inscription in his *Collected Stories 1939-1976*), I have spent every summer in Tangier, often in the

165

apartment directly beneath him, where his late wife, the writer Jane Bowles, used to live. It is, naturally, a pleasure to see him every day for months at a time; we have even concocted a system of rhythmic taps on the walls to signal when either of us wants to visit.

My days are spent at the little concert hall of the French Cultural Centre, an ideal place for composing. In late afternoon I sometimes go with Paul to the colourful Fez Market, in his golden, vintage 1966 Mustang, with the redoubtable Abdelouahaid Boulaich, his long-time driver, at the wheel. For company in the evenings, aside from Paul, I can usually rely on getting together with friends who live in or regularly visit Tangier, at restaurants (especially the one run by the hospitable Mercedes Guitta), cafés, beach bars and private homes. Among these people are: David Herbert, second son of the Earl of Pembroke, whom Paul has described as the city's 'unofficial social arbiter'; the young Guatemalan writer Rodrigo Rey Rosa, whose books Paul has translated; the American painter and writer Buffie Johnson, who has often allowed me the use of her apartment; the English writer and adventurist Gavin Young; the Italian composer and Trieste Opera director, Baron Raffaello de Banfield; Paul's preferred French translator, Claude-Nathalie Thomas; the British-born novelist, biographer and screenwriter, Gavin Lambert; the American poet Ira Cohen; the English tycoon Martin Soames; the former director of Tangier's French Cultural Centre, Georges Bousquet; an American college student, Kenneth Lisenbee, whom Bowles in one of his books nicknamed 'Krazy Kat' after the 1930s cartoon character; the American photographer Chérie Nutting; the Moroccan musician from Jajouka, Bachir Attar, who has recorded with the Rolling Stones; and the young American playwright Steven Diamond, inclined to make flying visits from Indonesia. Many of these friends were introduced to me over the years by Paul, for it seems that anyone of interest who arrives in Tangier eventually gravitates to his apartment.

Paul and I occasionally exchange books and discuss authors (we share, for example, a taste for the psychological suspense novels of Patricia Highsmith and Ruth Rendell, and the literate thrillers of Graham Greene and Norman Lewis), and he enjoys gossip, especially if *louche* or grotesque. But the main topic is usually music: his, mine, that of our various contemporaries. This is perhaps what sets me apart from his other friends in Tangier. We often listen to music together. He has long had a machine to play cassette tapes and now there is one for compact discs.

If, as the American composer, essayist and one-time Tangier resident Ned Rorem has proposed, all concert music is either of French or German orientation, then Paul's personal taste runs - as does his music - decidedly to the former. Ravel, Poulenc and Copland please him, Beethoven, Mahler and Schoenberg do not. He likes music that charms, and has aimed for that effect in his own scores, which are often inflected by jazz and blues (for instance, the *Six Latin-American Pieces* for piano, the *Concerto for Two Pianos, Winds and Percussion*, many of the songs). In considerable contrast are his novels and stories, in which the atmosphere sometimes verges on the horrific. Once, I asked him about this strange dichotomy, and he explained: 'The music and the books come from different compartments of the brain. They are quite separate.' In creating fiction, he said, one inevitably writes about people, and 'hostility can emerge'. Conversely: 'Music is about music - a closed cosmos existing only in musical terms.'

When not listening to music, Paul is given obsessively to tapping out polyrhythms with his fingers, even drumming on the roof of his car during outings in the countryside. Although he has composed little during the last four decades, he retains a musician's most basic instincts. Still, he was puzzled by Rorem's odd prediction, in an article, that his light, entertaining music would outlast his serious, nihilistic fiction. 'Is that supposed to mean that my books are of no importance?' he asked.

In New York I meet many musicians, both composers and performers, and with pianists it seems natural to promote Paul's attractive keyboard music. Several years ago I had a hand in arranging for some of it to be recorded on a Dutch label. More recently, Ramon Salvatore, an American pianist who has performed my own works, released an album that includes Paul's *Six Latin-American Pieces* and the first recording of *Carretera de*

Estepona. In the summer of 1991, with the co-operation of the genial Georges Bousquet and the French Cultural Centre, Salvatore came to Tangier to present an all-American recital that featured several Bowles pieces (along with works by Copland, Virgil Thomson, John Corigliano and myself). Paul and I and Krazy Kat attended it together. The hall was packed with Moroccan, French and American residents (the English found other things to do) and a few dozen tourists, and the evening was a success despite an ancient, ailing piano. Paul was much applauded after his music was played, and again at the end of the concert. (For a poster announcing the singular, perhaps even historic, event, he had provided the following typically laconic statement, which was reproduced in his own handwriting: 'The composers represented on this unusual program, apart from being natives of the United States of America, have in common the fact that all of them, at one time or another, sojourned here in Tangier.')

Copland, as noted, thought Paul to be 'something of a cold fish'; and, certainly, an impression of dourness was widely disseminated a few years ago by the publication of a hopelessly inaccurate and rather malicious biography. It is undeniable that many pictures show him looking grim, for he dislikes photo sessions. But there is another, very different side rarely seen by those who don't know him well - a cordial, even affectionate, Paul Bowles, his manner spilled by a remarkable sense of humour. To illustrate: ever since Bernardo Bertolucci filmed *The Sheltering Sky* in 1990, Paul has been pestered not only by the usual visiting lunatics of every stripe, but by journalists, academics and documentary film-makers. Few of these strike him as being passably intelligent or congenial ('Journalists refuse to verify or check. They're certain they're right.'), but he is none the less always coolly polite. He does not relish being bored, however, and during late-night get-togethers at his flat with close friends, his acid-laced remarks about the day's intruders can be quite funny, as can his mimicking of the singular piping voices of such deceased celebrities as Truman Capote and Virgie Thomson.

In a special category are Paul's imitations of various unsavoury birds; his reproduction of the raucous 'speech' of various African Grey parrots that he has owned approaches high comedic art. There is also a story of which I never tire, in which Paul describes, with feline hisses and growls, how a cat belonging to the composer Peggy Glanville-Hicks stalked him through room after room of her home, until in desperation he barricaded himself in a cupboard. Another tale concerns a Moroccan maid who was convinced that *djenoun* (evil spirits) lived in the cold-water pipes of Paul's apartment. One day he noticed her cleaning the toilet, cautiously removing water from the bowl with towels. When he pulled the chain to demonstrate a more sensible method, the rush of water so terrified the poor woman that she emitted a sonorous shriek (rendered spectacularly by Paul) and ran from the sinful Nazarene's flat, hysterically waving her arms in the air.

One evening Paul, Krazy Kat, Steve Diamond and I were walking to Casa Italia, a restaurant located in an old Moroccan palace not far from the Itesa. As we descended a steep, unlit street, we heard behind us a faint, somehow sinister, metallic sound, gradually coming closer. 'What's that?' asked Krazy Kay nervously. 'I don't know,' answered Steve. 'If we slow down until it catches up with us, we'll find out,' I suggested. Rolling out of the gloom came a solitary Coke can. It proceeded to keep pace with us. Whispered Paul: 'I think we're being bugged.'

He can also be amusing about himself. Cautious, to say the least, about his finances, he is fond of accusing me of 'spending money like a drunken sailor' - this because I frequently dine out. One day, after he had grumbled about a one-dirham price rise (about twelve cents) for some household item at the Fez Market, Steve affectionately dubbed him 'The Cheapskate of Tangier'. Weeks later, Chérie happened to mention the city's most expensive and pretentious restaurant, which provoked me to put on a severe face and inquire of Paul: 'Just when, sir, are you going to treat all your friends to dinner at the Marquis?' His retort, delivered with the slyest of smiles, was: 'But how *could* I do such a thing? It would be too out of character for the Cheapskate of Tangier!'

Paul is literal-minded to a surprising degree, and therefore vulnerable to pranks. I didn't fully appreciate this until 1988, when a collection of his new short stories appeared. One story, 'Hugh

Harper', concerns a British resident of Tangier whose eccentricity 'consisted in a taste for human blood', which he kept in the refrigerator and was in the habit of offering as refreshment to guests. This struck me as one of Paul's funniest tales. He said it had been inspired by an actual person. 'Should another vampire appear in Tangier,' I observed, 'it would serve you right if you were paid a visit.'

In the spirit of his story, I wrote him a preposterous letter on local hotel stationery, posting it as I left for a few days in Fez. It follows, grammatical, syntactical and orthographical grotesqueries intact:

> Dear M. Bowles,
>
> My nomen is Marjan C. van Vroonz of Utrecht. I am collectur of finger-nail, to-nail and the hair of noses of the great men. Also other things and liquids.
>
> A delightsful, woman - Mlle. Chérie Nooty - has telled to me that you emjoy provide her with to-nails and to write in your books of peoples drink blod for the apertif. May I to visit you soonest, extrat some to-nail and the other parts you permit, and to drink blod? I am pay for do this, 50 Guilders, may be 100, if blod explode me.
>
> I come you Samedi, at 5 afternoon with my machine. Plese to be not with clothes, and to be there disenfiction liquid, this important.
>
> Good-By.
>
> in respects,
> Mlle. Marjan C. van Vroonz

Returning late that Saturday (Samedi) afternoon, I unpacked and went up to see Paul. For a long time there was no answer to my knocks. Then the door slowly opened on the chain. Paul peered out apprehensively, and said: 'Oh, it's you. I was afraid it might be Mademoiselle van Vroonz.' Laughing, I responded: 'But surely you knew that letter was a joke, that I'm Mademoiselle van Vroonz!' In his best George Raft tough-guy voice, he shot back: 'Oh yeah? So where's your blood machine?'

During the fall and winter we keep in touch by mail (although, owing to the fantastical nature of the Moroccan postal service, letters can take anything from four days to four weeks arriving) and, sometimes, telephone. Paul's correspondence tends to be dry - or at least to the point. After he had endured three weeks of heavy winter rain:

> ... I don't mind bad weather if I can stay in and be comfortable. But that was made impossible by copious leaks in the ceiling of every room, which resulted in lakes underfoot, rugs soaked, water running onto my bed. It rained day and night without cease. Mold grew in white fluffs on the furniture, the water dripped into the middle of the salon, undeterred by the fire in the fireplace. As I write this, there is no dry place to put my feet; the water drips regularly into a line of bowls and kitchen receptacles beside me. This house is clearly jinxed.

About my proposed plan - never, alas, implemented - to sabotage a recital by an ex-friend, a pianist whose trade mark is memory lapses, he wrote: 'I loved the idea of you seated in the front row at [his] concert, holding the scores in full view and evincing amazed disapproval throughout the duration of the music. It would make a very funny scene in a film.'

Learning I had attended a reading by a writer we both admire: 'So you finally met [X] - caught her in the undignified act of signing her books en masse. I wonder why she stoops to that, need of money?'

Responding - with what he termed 'my only limerick' - to a testy verse I sent him when the South African novelist Nadine Gordimer was awarded the 1991 Nobel Prize for Literature:

> 'There was a young girl named Nadine
> Who felt that mankind was unclean
> A day is a night
> And a black man is white
> In Miss Gordimer's African scene.'

171

On the domestic front: 'I'm delighted with my new maid, now that the old one has made away with everything.' Also:

Abdelouahaid [Paul's driver] took it into his head to go out and buy me a new stove, claiming that the one I have now is no good. He's fairly right, but he just came to deliver a new one, which proved to be too big to fit into the place reserved for it, so he's gone away to look for another. Chaos in the kitchen! He was supposed to bring a chicken, but he failed to do that. A stove is so much bigger and more expensive. Unfortunately it's made of iron and enamel, and I can't have it for lunch.

Reacting to a piano piece (from my *Epigrams, Book 2*) dedicated to him: 'No. 5, *Demonic*, sounds the most difficult of the lot, but I imagine that's not what you want to know; rather whether I think it *resemblant*. (Although it's not a portrait. It's the composer's idea of the subject, no?) In any case, it's pleasingly violent.'

Concerning an invitation to the West African nation of Mali, the scene of his recent short novel, *Too Far from Home*: 'That's all I need, to live in a place where the population is entirely animistic and the witch-doctors consult tortoises to help diagnose the ills of their patients. It might not be too different from Tangier.'

For Paul, in his favourite role of passive spectator, Morocco has been a congenial milieu - a continuous peep-show of the chaotic, where the delicious possibility of violence always lurks in the wings. The numerous illogicalities of Muslim society, maddening to many Westerners, intrigue and amuse him. Writing in his autobiography, *Without Stopping*, of his initial visit so long ago to that extraordinary land, he approvingly notes its intrinsic theatricality, 'the impression of confusion and insanity'. 'I knew,' he concludes, 'I would never tire of watching Moroccans play their parts.'

The essence of more than a few of his books has, after all, derived from nearly half a century's residence in Morocco. Even

172

today, Paul will sometimes sit at the Café Tingis in Tangier's Socco Chico, sipping a mint tea and noting the bizarre behaviour of denizens of the Medina. As he walks through the narrow casbah alleys, his novelist's eye misses nothing: no drama goes unremarked, no peculiarity unseen, no lunacy unappreciated.

He complains that his adopted country - and especially Tangier, where ugly new high-rise buildings sprout everywhere and fast-food restaurants invade the once-classy Boulevard Pasteur - has become far too modern and Americanised; that one must now travel far south, to the pre-Sahara, for remnants of the old, the primitive, the real. But despite this outrage (which may even gratify his innate pessimism), I doubt he would be happier elsewhere. Never mind that his roof leaks, his maids steal, prices rise, doctors are homicidal and hordes of journalists beard him in his den. Paul Bowles lives on in Morocco.

PAUL BOWLES BY HIS FRIENDS
(£12.95)
Edited and with an introduction by Gary Pulsifer

This tribute to the writer Paul Bowles contains contributions by: Francis Bacon, Melvyn Bragg, William S.Burroughs, John Cage, Ira Cohen, Gregory Corso, Anne Cumming, Millicent Dillon, Ruth Fainlight, Lawrence Ferlinghetti, Charles Henri Ford, Allen Ginsberg, David Herbert, Patricia Highsmith, John Hopkins, Buffie Johnson, Gavin Lambert, Nicholas Lezard, Marguerite McBey, Joseph A.McPhillips III, Peter Owen, James Purdy, Phillip Ramey, Richard Rayner, Edouard Roditi, Ned Rorem, John Ryle, Maria St Just, Emilio Sanz de Soto, Stephen Spender, Claude-Nathalie Thomas, Gore Vidal, Terry Wilson and Gavin Young.

Available by Paul Bowles: CALL AT CORAZON £13.50. LET IT COME DOWN £14.50, MIDNIGHT MASS £13.95, THE SHELTERING SKY £13.50, THE SPIDER'S HOUSE £15.50, A THOUSAND DAYS FOR MOKHTAR £13.95, UP ABOVE THE WORLD £14.50, POINTS IN TIME £6.95, THEIR HEADS ARE GREEN £13.95, WITHOUT STOPPING £18.50, TWO YEARS BESIDE THE STRAIT £6.95

By Jane Bowles: PLAIN PLEASURES (first edition) £35.00, THE COLLECTED WORKS OF JANE BOWLES £15.95

Translated by Paul Bowles:
Mohammed Mrabet: M'HASHISH £4.50, THE BIG MIRROR £4.95, LOOK AND MOVE ON £12.95
Isabelle Eberhardt: THE OBLIVION SEEKERS £4.50
Rodrigo Rey Rosa: THE BEGGAR'S KNIFE £4.50, DUST ON HER TONGUE £8.95, THE PELACRI PROJECT £12.95

Peter Owen Publishers, 73 Kenway Road, London SW5 0RE
(071-373-5628)

Sara al Nawwaf
SURPRISE

Translated by Peter Clark

In one of the public parks. . . on a bench. . . Nura sat with her friend Salwa, who never went out without a veil, in accordance with her husband's instructions.

Anyone who saw them would think that they had come for a moment of quiet relaxation, but Nura kept looking at her watch as if she was expecting something to happen or was waiting for somebody. Nura murmured to herself, "It's six o'clock, the time Khalid got in touch with me the first time." Then she smiled and looked down at the grass just in front of her. She gazed at it as if she were at the cinema.

*   *   *

"Hello. . . who's that?"

A husky voice answered, "I. . . I want to get to know you."

"You must be one of those wicked young men who have nothing better to do than pester girls," she answered nervously.

She put the receiver down and tried to carry on reading. . . but the phone rang again. She reached out for the receiver. . . but hesitated, "He must be one. . . what does the fellow want?" She left the room so she could read without being disturbed.

A week went by and she was in a state of nerves. The fellow would not give up contacting her. Each time she put the receiver down as soon as she heard his voice. She became obsessed by the man and decided to have a word with him. . . if only to find out what he was after. The phone rang again. Nura paused just a second and then picked up the receiver. Yes, it was the same voice.

"What do you want from me?"

"I told you," the young man replied, "I want to get to know you."

"What do you want to get to know me for? Have you ever seen me? Do you know my family?"

"No, I don't know you. I felt bored, picked up the phone and dialled your number at random and when I heard your voice I was enchanted and made up my mind to get to know you. That's why I keep on phoning you."

"You get bored?" Nura said, surprised. "But you are a man and you've got everything going for you - you can go to clubs, you can drive out of town for a picnic and so on. . . it's the girls who get bored by all the routine around them."

The man realised that the door was open to a dialogue. "How can you say that a girl gets bored with routine?" he asked her.

Nura was eager to give an answer but her mother called out and she became confused. "I'll get in touch this time tomorrow," the young man said. Nura agreed and put the receiver down, hoping her mother had not noticed. Too late. Her mother asked her who she was talking to. She said it was a girl-friend who wanted Nura to go and see her.

"Ask your father," her mother said. "If he says you can go, you can go."

"Father. . . Father will of course say, 'No, a girl's place is at home'."

"Your father is right."

"You go along with Father on everything. Even when he took a second wife. . . and a third. You just smiled and said Father had his rights - but don't you have your rights? And don't I have any rights? He refused to let me finish at the University and wouldn't let me be a teacher and doesn't even let me go and see my only friend. . . he doesn't even let me do that."

"What do you want to do, then? Go against your father?"

"My father wants me to be a prisoner at home. Then after a while he'll marry me off to some man I don't know and I'll go from one prison to another."

"But your husband may be different. . . He may let you finish University and go out to work."

Nura smiled bitterly. "Maybe he will be different," she said. "Or maybe he'll be the same. . . or even worse. . . who knows?"

A few days later Nura was feeling fed up with everything and did not know what to do with herself. The phone rang. Nura raced to it. She heard the young man's voice and felt thrilled to bits. At last here was a way of having some fun and cheering herself up. There was no danger if it was simply a telephone conversation. There could be no problem. It was all perfectly easy.

Nura talked to the young man. He was called Khalid, she learnt, unmarried and without any sisters. She told him about herself and about how bored she got, about her father who believed that a woman's place was in the home. There were more calls and a relationship was built up. Nura felt full of happiness whenever he got in touch for she was always in and without anything else to do. She suffered from idleness. The telephone relationship went on for several months and then Khalid said he wanted to see her, saying, "I've grown to love your voice but I want to see the girl whose gentle voice has made me fall in love with her."

Nura smiled at these fine words. "But we'd be seen," she told him.

"Don't be afraid. Why don't you come to the park with a friend?"

"All right then, with my friend. . . but I have to wait for her to get in touch with me. My father has padlocked the dial."

She made the commitment and waited for her friend, Salwa, to call. Two days went by before she got in touch. She told her about the rendezvous. The two friends discussed it and agreed in the end to the idea of meeting in the park. Nura joyfully passed the news on to Khalid.

"I've never seen you before," he said, "so how can I tell you from any other girl in the park?"

Nura thought for a moment. "Ah yes, I know," she said. "My friend's face is totally veiled because that's what her husband wants. You can then tell that it's us."

She heard him laughing on the phone. "Then you'll come

along with a knight in armour," he said.

Nura laughed when she heard the term, knight in armour. "Yes, I'll come along with her."

"And I'll turn up with a friend in a white car. You'll be able to tell it's us because the car's windows are smoked."

Nura rang off.

* * *

She is now in the park, waiting for him to come.

"Nura," her friend said, "maybe he'll let you down and not turn up."

"Khalid can't possibly let me down. He loves me. He told me so. And he. . . Look, there's a white car. He's coming. Let's go, I'm scared."

Nura did not know what to do and felt unable to move. But she got up with Salwa and went towards the white car. She thought to herself with a smile, "Khalid will see the knight in armour."

Before they reached the car the door opened and a young man got out, smiling. Nura smiled back, but was then taken by surprise when Salwa cried out, "Abdullah? What's this you're up to?"

She raised her veil. The young man was then shaken at the sight of her. He was lost for words.

Nura looked at her friend. "Who is this Abdullah?" she asked. "Do you know him? Who is he?"

"My dear, Abdullah is my husband. Don't you see? This is my husband who insists I go around veiled so nobody can see me. But he's not just content with looking at girls, but he dates them! That's my faithful husband."

She threw her veil on to the ground and stormed off, leaving her husband and her friend, baffled and motionless.

Emily Nasrallah
MORNING STAR

Translated by S. V. Attala

I approach your presence on tiptoe, whispering your name, asking your permission to tell the story.

Now that everything is over: dust has returned to dust, and the spirit to its creator, and the face that once shone like a star has faded. . .

(Her face, in her youth, was like the morning star on a summer dawn.) The sky-blue eyes, the lips set in an expression of tenderness, the forehead and nobly lifted head crowned with chestnut hair set in a chignon, the fashion in those days.

They married her off young. (For a girl to remain unmarried past the age of fifteen was a disgrace to the tribe.) Such were the ideas of her kin, and they married her off at fourteen, on the brink of decline. She wouldn't lift her eyes to his face. (For all her sparkling beauty, Khazma was scared of her own shadow. Quiet, cautious in her choice of words, she spoke only when it was vital.) Her demands remained modest, since she rarely conversed with others. Others spoke for her, made decisions in her stead.

"Is Khazma back from the garden?"

"She's back."

"Has she foddered the cattle?"

"Yes."

"Has she filled the urn from the spring?"

"She filled it early this morning."

"Where is she now?"

"In her corner, embroidering a tablecloth."

"Embroidering? There's time for embroidery?"

"She's finished her chores, and she's resting."

"Resting! Well, let her rest."

And her mother would get up to complete the chores that awaited her, too, wherever she turned, and not a word of the dialogue would filter through to Khazma's ears.

But who is to say that the words remained secret after all, that the chinks of doors and the cracks in walls didn't leak the forbidden words through to her in secret? Who is to say that she stayed in her corner, embroidering, whenever she sensed the echo of those stern questions? Pressing her ear to the door, she would listen, hearing everything they said about her, just as she was to hear, later, the dialogue between the head of the tribe and his forbearing wife:

"Faris Mu'iz will be visiting us."

"He will receive a warm welcome."

"You welcome him without asking why he's coming?"

"I know why he's coming."

"And what's your opinion?"

"My opinion is yours. I follow your lead."

"He's a good man, decent; he can provide her with everything a girl needs: comfort, security, ample means, and a shield for her honour."

"Shall we ask her opinion?"

"Her opinion? Don't put ideas into her head."

"Maybe you're right."

"Of course. I always am."

She drew away from the door, choking on her frustration. She wished there were some bridge between her and her mother, some way to pour out her heart and mind to her, to tell her what she thought of Faris Mu'iz, of her father and kin, of being the prisoner of such solitude and emptiness.

But no such opportunity was granted her, nor did it cross her mother's mind when she took her aside to broach the subject.

"Faris Mu'iz will be visiting us this afternoon; find yourself a corner to hide in." (It was usual for girls to avoid the eyes of those seeking a wife. Wife, partner, companion - such were the names that applied to these girls, born into families that drifted through time without ever taking a step towards progress or change. The girls would hide, peering through a crack in the window or chink in the door, hoping to overhear the conversations that would determine their fates.)

Faris Mu'iz arrived, and with him his aging mother and the village elder. Her father and mother greeted them. They had gathered together the elders of their family, sent the youngsters out of the house, and locked the door on Khazma. In that solitary hiding place, alone with her curiosity, she strained with every ounce of her energy to hear what was being said.

They spoke well of her. She was especially roused to hear words of praise from the mysterious stranger. His voice stirred her deeply: We are honoured to be considered your kin. We have heard so much about her. An honourable girl, with a reputation as fragrant as musk and ambergris. Beauty is secondary to me, although she has it in abundance. Beauty of character is more important.

Myself? Yes, I saw her once returning from the spring. (Khazma, on a summer evening, lifting the urn to her head, her slender boyish figure swaying like a palm tree heavy with fruit. Her thickly-plaited hair bounced at her shoulders as she walked between her companions like a budding rose, towering over the other flowers around her.)

I saw her with her friends, but she alone caught my eye. At once I knew my heart was set on her. I said to myself, "You've travelled far, but God has rewarded you: this is the girl of your dreams." Now the matter is in your hands; I await your approval.

There was a moment of silence, in which Khazma feared they would hear her heartbeats, pounding within her like gypsy drums. They were deciding her fate. Sitting there, behind closed doors, deciding her fate, awaiting her father's answer.

The stranger spoke again: "I'd like to hear her mother's opinion."

Her mother answered in a subdued voice: "I am in agreement with her father."

Her father coughed. (She knew this habit of his; it always preceded his irrevocable decrees.) He coughed and cleared his throat, and said, "We are honoured to welcome you into the family."

Her heart plunged, stood still. She could scarcely absorb the meaning of his words, scarcely begin to imagine the effect that this simple verdict would have on her. Hearing the key in the lock, she hurried back to her seat in the corner, trying to compose herself. Her mother entered, beaming.

"Congratulations, Khazma! Congratulations, dear. This is a once in a lifetime opportunity. A handsome young man, energetic, with a good reputation, and rich... yes, rich, Khazma... be happy, my dear; follow him to the ends of the earth, live in luxury, make up for the deprivation of your mother, who lived her life on crumbs. Look at my hands... see the cracks between my fingers? Look at these palms. These aren't the fingerprints of happiness. These are the autographs of misery and toil, of the pain that will hold me hostage for the rest of my days.

"Khazma, your father has been a good husband, but my life is miserable, my darling. They told me marriage was heaven on earth, but for me it was a sentence to hard labour... a sentence that will continue till the end of my life."

Her mother chattered on, weeping, wiping her tears with her chapped palms. Khazma felt distant, unable to reach her or grasp her words. As though she had not quite finished gathering together her scattered self.

She watched her silently, without moving her lips.

"You stare at me and say nothing!" her mother exclaimed. "We did this for your sake. What do you think? He asked me, as he was leaving, he said quite frankly, these are his very words, he said, 'I respect your opinion, and her father's, naturally, but I'd like to hear what the girl thinks.'

"Now that you're engaged to him, you can talk to him, and tell him what you think if he asks you. So tell me, what are you going to say?"

Khazma opened her mouth and forgot to close it. Her eyes kept blinking as she stared at her mother, unable to control the expressions passing over her face. Now they were asking her opinion? What difference did her opinion make now? She was already engaged to him! And her mother had burnt all the bridges behind her, leaving her no option for retreat.

He returned the next day. Khazma's mother brought her out to greet him, and then left them alone together. He looked at her tenderly, something she was unaccustomed to in those around her.

"Now that we're engaged, I'd like to hear your thoughts. What do you think of me, for example? Are you happy?"

Khazma nodded dumbly. Her eyes stung. The world around her was burning, yet here he was, with those tender eyes and that gentle touch, offering her a future. Inviting her to brave the torrent and plunge in. She couldn't swim; she had scarcely ventured near the water before. Yet his hand, gripping hers, was saying, "Lean on me; I won't let you drown." She heard again her mother's words: Marriage was a sentence to hard labour. Yet this man, sitting before her, came from a land of fragrant promises; on his arm she would transcend every obstacle.

His voice brought her back to the present.

"I know there's a difference in age between us, but we won't let that matter. I'll spoil you like a daughter."

He was promising her the comfort she longed for, the paradise her impassive, emotionless father had never offered.

He was so close, a hair's breadth away. He pulled her against him. Feeling the warmth of his body run through her, she went limp, yielding to the arm around her waist.

"You're beautiful. Look at me. Don't be shy."

Her eyes fluttered, but she couldn't look up. She kept her gaze lowered as a delicious shiver ran through her. His whisper tickled her ear:

"Please. Look at me."

Very shyly, she looked up at him with the eyes of an obedient child, yielding herself trustingly to a warm lap. He startled her with a hug that stirred her to her depths, and a kiss that burrowed through her lips to the very bottom of her heart.

Instinctively she backed away. Finding nowhere to turn, she froze in place.

"Don't be afraid," he insisted gently. "I won't hurt you. I'll take care of you. These arms will carry you to paradise."

And a few days later he did carry her off, far from her homeland.

He alone accompanied her to the strange new world of which she knew nothing but the name, and a vague sense of mystery.

"A beautiful bride."

"A real beauty, that Khazma. A treasure."

"A rare catch! Where did you find her?"

His friends, in this strange country, expressed their opinions of the prize he had brought back.

"Faris, you knave! You've been busy!"

"What they say is true: the mines back home hold the brightest jewels."

Khazma glowed to hear their praise, her parched heart drinking in their words like dew.

Faris was not as pleased. His jealousy stirred, and tenderness gave way to suspicion. Soon his doubts found their way into action.

"You're not to leave the house without me, you understand? You're still young; you don't understand the way things work in America. You're my responsibility, so if you want to be happy you had better obey me."

His words threw her off balance. Lost, she longed for the old country. But what remained for her there? Not one corner had been left unspared by fire. . .

And so she slowly retreated, gave up all ambition. Besides, a new life was growing within her. Immersing herself in her preparations, she discovered that this tiny new being could free her from her prison cell, and restore her to a world of dreams.

And the dreams piled up, and the years passed.

The number jumped to six. Three sons, she bore him, and three daughters, and there was no longer time to weep over the past.

*   *   *

And so Khazma lived out her life in a cocoon, isolated from others' eyes. It was a cocoon spun by the man who had seduced her with his tenderness, plucking her like a flower out of the gardens of her old country.

Her children grew up, one by one, and made their way out into the world, while she alone remained, the companion of solitude and silence.

The passing years were like a dark film over her eyes, clouding her sight, hampering her motion.

People no longer mentioned her, except occasionally to sigh over her beauty, wasted in the shadow of a selfish jealousy.

But things change, even inside cocoons, and in one day, in one moment, everything changed for Khazma.

Faris died.

Her husband, her gaoler, the arbiter of her destiny.

He who had carried the scales of justice, of punishment and reward. And Khazma swung her head from side to side (and the chignon, now gray, but still styled in the fashion of her youth, swung with her), and she found only emptiness around her. Bewildered, she found herself suspended in mid-air, hanging by a thread that could snap at any moment.

She wept until she had no more tears to cry. And then she turned inward upon herself, and sat in a corner, refusing to budge. Her children tried to no avail to restore her to the natural world that renewed itself with the sunrise every morning.

One day her daughter arrived from a distant city, and, without asking, scooped her up in her arms and carried her to her car.

"You're going with me, to spend some time with your grandchildren."

She looked at her daughter's determined face and knew there was no changing her mind.

She had come to bring her out of her isolation, to help her

plant her feet on the ground once again.

Impulsively she reached out to touch her own legs. Could it be that blood was really coursing through them again?

"What's the matter, Mother?" her daughter asked, noticing her movement.

"Nothing, dear," she said hesitantly, "Nothing. But on your way, I wish you would drive by the graveyard. I need to ask your father's permission before I go."

Nawal el-Saadawi
THE VEIL

I came to suddenly and found myself sitting with a bottle of wine in front of me which was nearly empty and an ashtray full of cigarette butts of an unusual kind I had never seen before. Then it struck me that they were my new cigarettes, which I had started smoking three or four years before.

I raised my head from the ashtray and saw a man I had never seen before. He was naked except for a silk gown which was open and revealed a hairy chest and hairy thighs. Between his chest and thighs there was a pair of tight striped underpants which clung to him. I raised my astonished eyes to his face. Only then did I realise that I had seen him before. My eyes stared into his for a long time, and I smiled. It was a strange smile, spontaneous and fleeting, like a light or an electrical current passing across my face and leaving nothing behind but a strange type of anxiety resembling the eternal anxiety of man in his quest for God or happiness. Why should that flaw in my existence and my body appear at that precise moment? My eyes meet hundreds or thousands of other eyes every day, and yet the world remains just the same and my body does not change at all. My discomfort resembled man's eternal anxiety, but it was over quickly. My body returned to normal, and life went on like any other day. It had been three or four years since I first saw him. I had almost entirely forgotten him in the crush of work, home, and other people.

My eyes fell once more on his naked body and hairy thighs. My face was not the same when I looked at his body as when I looked at his eyes. My problem was that what I felt deep inside me showed immediately on my face. His eyes were the only part of his body with which I had a real link. They dispersed my alienation and loneliness. My relationship with him became a real one - in the midst of numerous other relationships which weren't. For three or perhaps four years every time I met him by chance on the street, in an office or a hallway, I stopped a moment to be astonished and perplexed. Then I would go on my way knowing that it was a very strange relationship, but at the same time a familiar and acceptable one in the midst of numerous relationships which were neither familiar nor acceptable.

When we started meeting on a regular basis, or at least a more or less regular one, my relationship with him did not extend to parts of his body other than his eyes. We would sit for long hours and converse while my eyes never left his. It was in effect a meeting of our minds. It was enjoyable, but the enjoyment still lacked something. What was it?

I asked myself if it was the desire of one body to contact the other body. Why not? When all is said and done, was he not a man and I a woman? The idea seemed strange, even novel to me. An obsessive desire to know took possession of me. What would it be like for my body to meet his? A fierce desire to explore can sometimes be even stronger than love. My curiosity might be strong enough to push me occasionally into an encounter without love. But each time I feel aversion. My intellect discovers that my body finds the man's body repugnant in every case except that of love.

I knew the reason for this aversion of mine. It is a natural one related not to my body but to human history. To the extent that man has worshipped his masculinity, woman has found him repugnant. Women's aversion to men is the other side of men's worship of a masculine god. There is no power in the world which can overcome this female aversion to men, unless love wins out over the male god, and history becomes as it was six thousand years ago when the deity was feminine. Had love won out? Was the relationship between us love? I did not know. I had no proof. Is love something you can prove? What about that desire to see his eyes, which found its way to the surface of my crowded life from time to time like that of a person who goes to a sacred spring to kneel and pray before returning home? But I am not a believer to kneel or pray or acknowledge any god except my intellect. What was drawing me to his eyes?

Or is love a legend, like the legend of Adam and Eve, Cinderella, the phoenix, and the unicorn? The day of legends is gone. The veil has dropped away from them leaving them naked. Many veils have dropped away from my intellect as it has matured. Whenever a veil falls, I weep for a night in sorrow over the beautiful fantasy which has been lost. But the next morning I find my eyes gleaming. The tears have washed them the way dew washes jasmine blossoms or the rose. I leave the mirror and walk upon the veil where it has fallen to the floor. I trample it underfoot even more vigorously than the day before.

* * *

He filled the glass for me the tenth or twentieth time. My hand trembled a little as I clutched the glass, but my intellect, the god inside my head, sat steadily, as motionless as the Sphinx. My eyes continued looking into his and did not look away, although I perceived - how, I don't know exactly - that he was no longer wearing the silk gown. It seemed also that he no longer had on the tight striped shorts.

I noticed that his body was white, infused with red. It bespoke power, health, daily hygiene, and good nutrition. My eyes must have stayed fixed on his, because I perceived after a moment that he had taken hold of my head with his hands to make my eyes look at his body.

I looked at him once again with my healthy 20-20 vision. I saw again his power and health, his clean, well-fed body. I almost told him how vigorous, powerful, clean and well-nourished he seemed.

But my eyes rose and met his. I do not know if he looked at me in astonishment or whether the astonishment was in my own eyes. I said to myself, of course it is an astonishing situation. It is past three a.m. The bottle of wine is empty. There's no one at home. The world outside is silent, dark, dead, non-existent. So what's keeping his body and mine apart?

When I moved my head in his direction, I saw him sitting. He was wearing the gown. Its belt was carefully fastened around his waist, concealing his chest and thighs. I could no longer see any of him except his head and neck and his feet in his light slippers. His face viewed from the side seemed burdened as though he he had become depressed suddenly or had grown old. His features had gone slack, like those of a child who is ready to go to sleep after unsuccessfully trying to stay up late. I stretched out my hand like a mother patting her child's face, and planted a compassionate, maternal kiss on his brow.

I went out to the street and raised my warm face to the cold, moist dawn breeze. I felt a mysterious sensation of pride mixed with a strange feeling of sorrow. I put my head on my pillow. My eyes were open and wet with tears. My intellect had been winning out over the wine, until I surrendered my head to the pillow, and then the wine triumphed. Grief was the victor over pride.

When I opened my eyes the next day, the effects of the wine had dissipated, and the covering had been blown away from my eyes. I looked at them in the mirror. They were glistening and washed with tears. I was about to leave the mirror as usual and trample on the fallen veil under my feet, to stamp on it with renewed energy. But I did not move from where I stood. I stooped over and plucked the veil off the floor. In my imagination I placed it once more over his face.

Liana Badr
RENDEZVOUS

Translated by S.V.Atalla

At last she would see him. At last she was here. A girl on top of a hill. The place remained tied in her memory to the gigantic ruins of Roman times. Endless amphitheatres of stone. And now she was here to see him, and to pass on the secret letters to the fedayeen. Every week one of the girls came here to Jarash, penetrating the siege that surrounded the area, bringing the bulletins, instructions inscribed in microscopic writing on papers stuffed into their clothes, penetrating the siege that surrounded the area. And now it was her turn, her chance to savour his face after his absence of two months or more. The narrow road writhed like a black snake in the suffocating heat of June. The dull pine trees with their sparse branches were listless as summer crickets. The girl sat on the stones of a fallen wall, waiting for some godsend to take her to the camp. A short while ago the taxi driver had turned back towards Amman, refusing to take her any further towards the sound of distant skirmishes. The sky was clear as crystal. Her fingers clamped tightly about the white bag she held, she imagined herself on the prow of an enormous ship, ploughing through that vast space of blue. No ruins; no amphitheatres or temples or stone arches, it seemed to her. Only the hill. The summit where she stood. The valleys dipping sharply away around her. Her unexpected solitude, and her swollen belly, a balloon that had landed abruptly on her body. For the tenth time she opened the bag in which she had put his clean underwear and his favourite brand of tobacco, rummaging through the items to make sure she had forgotten nothing. The professor's voice still rang in her ears:

"You're still a child yourself. I don't see why you're pregnant."

She had refrained from answering. What could she have said? She smiled at him with her bright eyes, her boyish haircut, the maternity dress with its pattern of roses and doves. A wide, mysterious smile. Carrying forgiveness, full of the hidden wisdom he couldn't grasp despite his years. She said nothing, not knowing how to say: The point is, professor . . . we are the revolution. Yes, us. Against everything. The defeat of June 1967. Old customs and worn-out traditions. Even our parents, who fight love more fiercely than they do imperialism and capitalism. Professor, I fell in love with him, and I married him, while still a child, as you say, because I want to be. We are the revolution, the new society. But why has my belly swollen this much? Love is romantic and wonderful. But pregnancy! My God! A public testimony to the dubious physical reality of intercourse. Like a crime! Professor, the guilt sticks to the roofs of our mouths no matter what we do, because they bring us up this way. But making love is one thing, and having babies is another thing altogether. It makes me resemble my mother, makes me older than I am, or want to be.

The rocks needled her legs where they pressed against the wall. Heat rose up towards her from the valley below like thirsty birds. Everything lay spread out before her as though displayed in the crystal ball of some ancient deity. The road's elbow, bent up towards the guerrilla base. The scattered trees. The dry remains of yellowing brush among the rocks. The silence of the blue dome reverberating within her to the echoes of distant gunfire. My God, as though this were not the Jarash she had heard of for so long. The driver must have let her off a good distance away from where there were people. A bird landed briefly at her feet. Its rounded belly looked steely-smooth. But she knew it wasn't so. Once she had kept a sparrow in a cage until she found its insides bleeding. Hajja Salima had told her that sparrows couldn't live in cages; she hadn't listened. Panting in the heat, she looked at her watch. How long would this go on? Two and a half hours; that was too much. And then! As though someone had heard her prayer. A military jeep passed by. "What is it, lady? No one to take you to the camp? We'll take you. But it would be better for you to head back to

Amman, wouldn't it?"

She got into the jeep. Bounce, bounce, thump, bang, wham . . . Her stomach muscles reacted to the quick turns. Something was shrinking and hardening inside her, throbbing, declaring its resistance as the jeep jolted over potholes and bumps. Forward! Halt! Here we are in the camp, lady. They were embarrassed to suggest that she jump. She understood. Jumped. Sprang out, bending her body, then unfolding it, a rainbow unfurling to its utmost.

So this was the camp. It seemed different from other camps. Greyer, more miserable. The colour of smoke, ashes, rock. Tin houses clustered together like miners' huts. Poverty overshadowed everything. No way to tell these houses apart, with their irregular shapes, the sheets of hammered tin taken from barrels and discarded cans. No clue to guide her to the one that had been described to her.

She wandered among the alleys looking for someone to direct her, but met no one. She realised how odd she must look, hopping over the open sewers that trickled through the deserted alleys. The wooden windows were shut. The crooked doors clung to the walls. Not a crack through which to pass to any inhabited place. The echoes of long-range artillery in some part of the camp. Army shelling, no doubt. Suddenly, from nowhere, a man with sinister features. He had a thick moustache and tousled hair. She had never expected things to come to this! For so long, she had dreamed of meeting her love in one of the caves in these hills. He would hold her close, while she clung to him and told him of the nightmares that had plagued her for so many lonely nights. Ever since that day in early May, when a neighbour had warned her about a secret intelligence agent frequenting the neighbourhood and asking for him by name. It was the beginning of a late spring in the capital with its seven hills and endless slopes. He had just finished showering in the little apartment tucked away from view. He told her the time had come for him to leave the city. Since September it had become a maze of traps laid out for the underground resistance leaders. He went, leaving the watch with the square face. He forgot it by the window, as though he secretly wished his wife would follow him to remind him of the escaping time. Alone, she had wrapped the watch with the ivory dial in the clean underwear she now carried. She wanted to hand it to him herself, looking just the way she did. Her comrades had made fun of her. You're going out to the wilderness like that, with your belly up to your chin? Well, what of it? she had said stubbornly. Why not? Don't I join in the secret operations every chance I get? Didn't I carry those banned directives around in perfect safety, stashed on top of my belly that's 'up to my chin,' as you say? Didn't I pass through dangerous blockades that even proven heroes, with no belly or anything of the sort, didn't make it through? No, she had expected at worst to encounter some treacherous blockade, some vital danger, not to end up where there was no one around but this suspicious man who was following her. She had thought it the utmost in misery, going to meet her love in a cave, surrounded by people cleaning their weapons with kerosene-saturated rags, where it would be difficult to complain to him about her troubled sleep. Even the baby! Imagine, he refuses to calm down when I finally go to bed; he keeps kicking, the monkey, as though he were in his own independent kingdom, not inside me. My God, even infants the size of your little finger gain their independence while they're no more than a bundle of cells. If he would at least listen to me and stay quiet for a while so I could sleep. The strange man approached her. Her heart beat faster. He must be from the secret intelligence agency. They were always following her in the city. Once she had been stranded in the attic of a lingerie boutique while one of them waited in the street outside. It took several hours for him to begin to doubt himself, dozens of sallies into the little store visited only by women, before he was convinced that she wasn't there after all. But the inhabitants! Where were the inhabitants? The man pursued her determinedly, narrowing the distance between them.

"Hullo there! Lady!"

She turned, trying to assess his identity through his very ordinary clothes. They were as nondescript as everything else around her.

"Who are you looking for, lady?"

"None of your business."

"Tell me. Who are you looking for?"

Suddenly his features relaxed in understanding.

"What organisation are you with, lady? Don't worry. I'm with security."

She explained what she wanted. In the condition you're in? No; you'll never make it up the hill. The clashes are intensifying. They'll be sweeping the camp in a matter of hours. The civilians are all in caves or in the shelters. The shelling will be getting heavier any minute. Turn over what you're carrying to your organisation's office. I'll show you where it is. You'd better leave at once, before the attack begins.

She insisted. I want to go up for ten or fifteen minutes. I don't care about the clashes. He looked at her belly, which he said was 'up to her ears.' He had known her for only a few minutes, and already he spoke to her like everybody else she knew, as though she were a stubborn child starting to act up. As if it were unnatural, what she wanted to do. He smiled and repeated: In the condition you're in? Impossible.

Taking her by the hand, as though he were an uncle, he led her to a hidden room were another strange man sat. This is your office; turn over the things and go home at once. Taking out the watch, she handed over the bag, urging the young man at the desk not to delay in sending the things up there, up to the men she wouldn't be able to reach. Her dream had become a negative of itself, everything she hadn't desired. She was pierced by a sharp longing for the smell of kerosene-saturated rags, rubbing the smooth bronze bodies of guns. She ached for the damp smell of the caves where the men were gathered. For the first time she was overcome by a dull awareness that her body was heavier than she was. It led her, it delineated her path and set her limits, and not vice versa. She had paid it no heed in the past. She used to run through the university quad in her flowing waistless dress of pink chiffon, a little girl's dress. Now her shape had changed. That was all there was to it. She had participated in demonstrations, marched long distances chanting with the women and schoolgirls, leaping off walls if need be when the army opened fire. But now!

Now!!

She headed toward the main road, searching for a car, in this empty world that seemed to have ended completely, to have been abruptly transferred up there, to the hills.

Then zzoo...oom! A bullet whizzed by her head. She felt it curve past her temple. From somewhere a man's voice came to her: Lady, drop your head and run! There's a sniper with long-range artillery who won't let anyone by here. She hollered back: Is there another way out?? No. Bend your head and run. Run...

She bent her head as far as she could over the unnatural belly that straddled her, and pushed her body forward, trying to run, but discovering that even that simple action was now beyond her. As though her body, preoccupied with making its baby, had forgotten about her, abandoned her. Even running! Impossible! She tried again, moving as fast as she could. But running. Running. Running? It had become her life's dream, all of a sudden, and she could no longer do it. Her Dr Scholl's slippers slid against her nylons as though she were walking on a soapy floor. The smooth wood slipped under her swollen arches, bloated with salt in this final month of pregnancy. It wasn't that she felt heavy. But she was trying, and no result! All this because of the damned slippers that were so comfortable on ordinary days. She could see nothing but the facades of shuttered shops on the main street, stretching out behind her, column after column. She felt as though she were swimming in a dense murky liquid. The terrycloth of her dress, gathered under her breasts, was constricting, suffocating. She was still in the same place; the only indicator of her speed was the sweat on her back and at the roots of her hair. For an instant she saw herself through the sniper's target-finder and hated the refreshing blue of her dress. If only she had worn the pink, it might have camouflaged her a little. During the demonstrations she had never cared. But here she was alone. Swimming slowly in a cloudy space. Trying to run in the dense fog of heat beneath a darkened sky in midday. Seeing nothing but columns one after another. Hearing nothing but bullets whizzing off the wall beside her. In front of and behind her. Pelting like popcorn. Opening to the fire, becoming white flowers. The distance was so long, and she was nowhere near its end.

Finally, the road. Safety. She walked along the asphalt, stopping to look back. The deserted camp looked like so many others whose inhabitants had been evacuated. So this was the city that was copper to the imagination. No. It was a tin camp. Tin, with no human breath in it. Only the rabid downpour of the sniper's fire, the squeak of fedayeen's rubber soles as they dashed through the alleys.

Once more she was standing by the roadside, finding another military jeep to transport her down to the hilltop where she had waited before. From there, over an hour later, she made out a car in the distance. A taxi from the city, an old Mercedes. Inside it, more village women than she could count, piled one on top of the other like braided hemp. She hesitated when the car stopped, almost deciding not to get in. My God, how could she fit on top of them? Where would they find room for her belly? She hesitated, but they shouted to her. Called to her to get in. They were ageless women, women who had lost their years in copper cities and tin camps, the features of their faces unfamiliar, cracked like stone, coated with mud and ashes, their black village garb still embroidered with the joyous patterns of the homeland. She squeezed in among them, wondering how many more people could fit into an ordinary car already carrying more than fourteen women, besides clucking chickens and trussed-up ducks.

By evening she was home. Elevating her swollen, blistered feet. Her friend Basima brought her lemonade, trying hard not to ask the question.

"Were you able to... did you... see him?"

She handed her the glass, switched on the radio. They listened: "Army forces pursued their advance into Jarash camp, in their attempt to purge it of all dissenters to the enduring principles of the Arab Nation and its undying national aspirations."

Jabra Ibrahim Jabra

Jabra Ibrahim Jabra
SINGERS IN THE SHADE

Translated by S. V. Atalla

The oud player was intoxicated with music and drink. Head bent over his instrument, he tweaked the strings, plucking them into a twanging resonance that rose and fell with the singers' voices.

Hands clapping, clapping, singing *Ala dalona, the north wind...* and sun dancing on the olive trees.

Dusty green trees, one after the other, on terraces sloping down to the road. Trees that could have been planted by the saints of past centuries, their twisted, knotty trunks and cracked grey beards intimate with time. When Sallum thought about it he felt a delicious lightheadedness, as though he approached the meeting-place of earth and sky beyond the distant blue mountains.

Of ya ba... sun dancing on thousands of green olive leaves, dusty to the touch, redolent of earth, like the stone on which he sat. Stones everywhere, greenish and white. Who could tell what hand had scattered them over the gentle slopes and down into the wide valley.

Men, women and children were singing and clapping. There were glasses of arrack in front of the older men, who sat crosslegged in a net of shade beneath the fine branches, singing *'Ala dal'ona*, then holding their breath while one singer let out the long *Ooof*, a sigh as long as eternity, full of all the nostalgia in the world, all the longing for loved ones who had passed on, never to be seen or touched again... *Ooof...* Sallum listened, only half understanding, to the singing that could wring longing and regret even from his seven-year-old heart. When he was as old as they were, he too would sit crosslegged under the olive tress on feast days, cradling the same strength and authority, the same longings and regrets.

Ooof... the men passed the bottle around, and one of the women got up to offer them more bread and white cheese and green olives...

Sallum's mouth watered, not so much at the sight of the appetisers as at the smell of rice and meat drifting from an enormous pot over the fire behind the singers, the fulfilment of the promise Musa had made him. But where was Musa?

Sallum glanced around, looking for his friend among the group of clapping singers, the women bustling about beneath a nearby olive tree, the heaps of baskets and bundles and plates. He couldn't see him anywhere. Finally he turned back to the distant pot. A crowd of boys and two or three women had gathered around it, breaking up firewood and stoking the flames, coughing from time to time when a gust of wind blew smoke into their faces. There among them was Musa, sitting on a rock, his eyes glued to the pot. Reassured, Sallum once again joined in the singing, clapping two or three times, then letting his eyes play over the steaming pot. The aroma of rice and meat teased his imagination, mixing from time to time with smoke and the faint fragrance of trees and earth.

Suddenly he realised that something hard that had been poking his thigh was about to fall out of his pocket. He grabbed it just in time and thrust it back in: he couldn't be seen with a crust of bread in a place like this, not when such a sumptuous meal was about to be served.

Ooo... Sallum wished he had the courage to join in this verse of *"Al-Mijana."* He and Musa and Elias often sat on the doorstep of some shop in town after it closed, acting out a performance. Holding imaginary instruments, they'd pretend to play. Then they'd start to sing *Ala dalona,* and Sallum would follow it up with a long *Ooof.* He didn't know many of the words, so he'd make do with:

*"The camels are laden
the camels are laden, the bells are ringing.
Ya layli ya layl."*

And every time, every time, he imagined the camels with
their arching necks and lofty heads lunging forward, their copper
bells, bell within bell, ringing all the long dusty way from his
town to the far-away olive trees, to the city beyond the hills, the
magical city he had walked to once with his father, with
breathtaking walls overshadowing cars and pedlars and people
sitting in cafés.

"Tomorrow's St George's Day."

Musa had said this to Sallum the previous afternoon. He had
reminded him several times. "There'll be lots of people there.
Elias's father pledged to slaughter a sheep if Elias got better. Have
you seen the sheep they bought?"

"Yes," said Sallum. "We took it a bag of grass from the fig
grove. So they're going to slaughter it tomorrow?"

"Yes. And they're going to cook it with rice, and give it away
to the people. There'll be singing after church, and then they'll
prepare the food."

"Are you going?"

"Of course. We'll get to eat rice and meat."

Sallum's mother had prepared lentil soup for supper that
evening. When Sallum found out he said to his mother, "Lentil
soup again? I'm tired of lentils."

"What do you want?" asked his mother. "Roasted chicken?"

"A bit of meat."

"Meat in the middle of the week, you monkey? I'll cook a
sheep's head and feet on Sunday."

"I'm tired of heads and feet. I want meat."

"You want a spanking! Your father works from sunrise to
sunset and never asks for such things."

"Why don't you buy us a bit of meat?"

"With what? The lice on your head?"

With a deep breath, Sallum took the plunge. "I'm going to
church tomorrow. Elias's father pledged to slaughter a sheep if

Elias got better. There's going to be lots of meat."

Sallum woke early to his parents' voices and the sound of his mother's slippers clicking back and forth across the bare floor. He threw off his blanket, its edge worn where he tucked it under his chin every night. Musa peeked warily through the door, then called in his thin voice, "Come on, Sallum. Aren't you up yet?"

Sallum jumped out of bed and pulled on his trousers and shirt.

"I haven't had time to patch your trousers yet," said his mother. Looking around at his brothers and sisters asleep on the floor, she turned to his father. "I can't keep up with them! Sallum's trousers aren't even a month old. He's a little devil - always climbing trees and rolling in the dirt. He doesn't take care of his clothes at all."

Sallum fingered the large patch on the seat of his trousers. His mother had cut it from a pair his elder brother had once worn.

After washing and having breakfast, Sallum and his friend walked through the vegetable patch and fig grove up to the road. Suddenly Sallum noticed that Musa had shoes on. "My mother doesn't know I'm barefoot," he said. "I hate shoes. But she makes me wear them Sundays and feast days."

"Wait a second and I'll run home and take off my shoes too," said Musa. "If my mother doesn't see me."

Musa set off running. Suddenly Sallum remembered something that sent him running home too.

"What brings you back?" asked his mother.

"I want a piece of bread," he said, heading for the bread-box. He took a piece that was three or four days old and shoved it into his tiny pocket. Then he ran out through the fig grove to the road again. A minute later Musa came running out barefoot too, and the two set off for St George's monastery as though headed for joy everlasting, their feet gradually whitening with dust.

Ooof... the dust on the olive branches seemed to vibrate with the long, quivering sigh that entwined men and women and children, expanding in ever-widening rings to encircle sun, shade, olive trees, and the singers beneath them. The steam from the pot rose with the melody, drifting into the air like a musical longing.

202

Sallum thought of the only song he knew:

> *The camels are laden*
> *the bells are ringing.*

He pushed his bare feet into the soil, savouring the damp cool beneath the surface, and imagined far-away bells ringing.

Suddenly Elias's mother appeared. "Time to eat!" she called to the men.

The singing stopped abruptly, the oud player strumming the strings two or three times more before noticing and laying his instrument aside.

In no time the straw mat was spread and the place filled with the clatter of dishes and the shouts of men and women laying out the food.

"A plate over here, a plate over there, a plate for Abu Samir. Abu Wadi', the bread! Spoons, spoons!" The spoons dropped onto the mat with a sharp clang that sounded good to hungry ears. The women turned the rice onto big platters crowned with chunks of meat, placing them on the mat in front of the men, where hands and spoons reached out to empty them into plates. A few boys tried to help themselves, but Elias's mother said sharply, "Kids, you eat later. Kids eat later. Men first. Where did all these kids come from? Good gracious!" The boys backed off to wait for the second serving. "Enjoy it!" said Elias's mother to the men. "Abu George, help yourself! Fill another plate for him. Some meat for Abu Abdallah..."

From his perch Sallum saw Abu George, round head bent over a belly that rested in his lap, lifting rice to his gaping mouth. Rice stuck in his moustache and the corners of his mouth; he shoved it in with a hunk of meat he held by the bone. His plate was filled again. Sallum's feet dug into the cool soil.

A few boys sidled up to the table again, but a man shouted, "Back off a little! Wait a little!" and a woman came to shoo them away. They scattered like a frightened flock of chickens. One of them stumbled over Sallum where he sat on the rock, his feet buried in the soil. Embarrassed, Sallum got up and backed away from his seat.

"Come on, girls!" Elias's mother called to the women. They came carrying fresh platters of rice, but this time they were less full and the pieces of meat crowning them were further apart. The men got up one after another to pour water from jugs and cans onto their hands, while women took the men's places, and boys crowded around the dishes.

Sallum felt a tremendous hunger, as though an abyss had opened up in his stomach and had to be filled. He got up and approached the food.

"Where did all these kids come from?" shouted Umm Wadi. "Have they no sense of shame?" She pushed away two boys she didn't recognise. Sallum, who was behind them, bumped into them, and as he tried to move forward her hand blocked his way. "Good heavens! One after another! Go get your mothers to feed you!"

At that, Sallum felt the abyss in his stomach close. He glimpsed Musa bent over the rice, stuffing his mouth with his hand, but he turned his back on the sight of the food, feeling he had been kicked aside like a dog. He walked off among the stones, slowly at first, then faster, finally breaking into a run, not knowing where he was heading, knowing only that he didn't want to hear the sounds of people eating behind him.

When he reached the monastery, he crossed to the far side of the old building where there was a fresh spring in the shade. He sat down on a rock, feeling a violent need to cry but determined not to. Taking the piece of bread from his pocket, he dusted it off and bit down on it. It was hard as a bone; his dry mouth couldn't break off a bite.

Bending over the spring, he let water run over the bread until it was wet all over. Cool, refreshing water splashed his feet, making fine patterns on his dusty legs. Standing up, he immersed his legs in the flow, chewing the wet bread and watching his feet gradually grow cleaner.

He soaked the bread again, and, feet dripping, sat on a nearby rock to finish his lunch. "A good thing I brought the bread," he thought to himself.

A little later he heard singers behind him. Clapping, ululation. A new song he hadn't heard before. Turning towards the voices, he remembered again the words of his song, *The camels are laden...*

"Laden with what?" he wondered aloud. He imagined the camels loaded with ballooning sacks, but couldn't tell what was in them. Suddenly Musa appeared, running towards him and calling, "Sallum!"

He quickly swallowed his last bite so Musa wouldn't know what had happened. "Don't you want to wash your feet?" he asked.

"Have you eaten?" asked Musa.

"Yes."

"Get any meat?"

"Of course."

"I only got a little piece."

"Makes no difference," said Sallum. "Big or little."

Musa washed his feet, took a drink from the spring, and joined his friend on the rock.

THE CONTRIBUTORS

S.V. Atalla is an aspiring poet and translator currently studying comparative literature at the University of California.

Liana Badr is a Palestinian novelist and short story writer currently living and writing in Tunisia. *Golden Hell* is her most recent collection of short stories. Previous works include *A Compass for the Sunflower*, translated into English in 1989. "The Meeting" is taken from "Liqa" in *Jahim Dhahabi [Golden Hell]*, published in Beirut by Dar al-Adab, 1991.

Vladislav Bajac was born in Belgrade, and lives there as a writer, translator and editor. His story, "The Tale About Lodging on the Way to Tuscany" appeared in *Passport 3*. *The Book of Bamboo*, from which we take this extract, is being published by Gallimard in France in March 1993.

Paul Bowles was born in New York but settled in Tangier with his wife, Jane, shortly after the war. He has been there ever since, and encouraged an interest in Arabic writing by translating the work of several authors into English.

Peter Clark has translated from the Arabic *Karari: The Sudanese Account of the Battle of Omdurman* by Ismat Hasan Zulfo (Frederick Warne, 1980) and *Dubai Tales* by Muhammad al Murr (Forest Books, 1991). He is also the author of *Marmaduke Pickthall, British Muslim* (Quartet, 1986). He has worked for the British Council since 1967 and from September 1992 has been Director, British Council, Damascus.

Ian Holmes has travelled extensively throughout North Africa and the Middle East and has contributed to *The Independent*. He is currently finishing his first novel and working on a book of travel poetry to be published in 1993.

Jabra Ibrahim Jabra is a widely renowned Palestinian novelist, poet, and critic of art and literature. Best known for his novels *The Ship*, translated into English in 1982, and *Hunters in a Narrow Street*, which he wrote in English and which was published by Heinemann, he has also produced three collections of poetry and numerous translations into Arabic, including *Hamlet* and Faulkner's *The Sound and the Fury*. "Singers in the Shade" was first published in Damascus in 1956, and has not previously been translated into English.

Thomas E. Kennedy's books include a novel, *Crossing Borders* (Watermark Press, 1990) and three books of literary criticism, the most recent an analysis of the short fiction of Robert Coover (Macmillan/Twayne, 1992). His stories, essays, poems, interviews, reviews and translations have been published widely in Europe and the USA. An American, he has lived in Denmark since the mid-1970s, and is European Editor of *Cimmaron Review*.

Ibrahim al Kouni is considered by many critics to be one of the most outstanding new Arabic writers. He has had three books published by the London-based Arab publisher, Riad el-Rayyes, and writes about the people of the southern Libyan desert.

James Lansbury was born in 1935 and lives in Huddersfield. His first novel, *Korzeniowski*, about Joseph Conrad, was published by Serpent's Tail in 1992.

Naguib Mahfouz is the outstanding novelist of the Arab world, and in 1988 was awarded the Nobel Prize for his achievements. His most famous work is *The Cairo Trilogy*, a monumental 1500-page epic about a Moslem merchant family. The two short stories printed here are both from his collection *Dunya-llah (The World God Created)*, not previously published in the UK.

I. van Mil is a journalist born in Holland, educated in Canada and now living in Essex. Her story, "Quo Vadimus, Daddy?", appeared in *Passport 2*.

Herta Müller was born in 1953 in Nitzkydorf, Romania, where a German colony from Suabia settled. Her mother tongue is German. She studied at the University of Temeswar in Romania and continued to live there until 1987 when she moved to Berlin. The stories here are from her first collection, *Niederungen*, comprising prose pieces that derive from the lives in a Romanian farming community. Her novel, *The Passport*, is published by Serpent's Tail.

Emily Nasrallah is a Lebanese novelist and writer of short stories and children's literature. Her works have dealt with such issues as the civil war in Lebanon, Arab women's roles and experiences, and the effects of emigration. One novel, *Flight Against Time*, and a collection of stories, *A House Not Her Own: Stories from Beirut*, have been translated into English. "Morning Star" is from *Najmat al-Sabah*, in *Al-Mar'a fi 17 Qissa [Woman in 17 Stories]*, published in Beirut by Mu'assasat Nawfal, 1984.

Sara al Nawwaf is the nom-de-plume of a writer from Dubai in the United Arab Emirates. She was born in 1965 and graduated in Psychology from the UAE University. She has written TV scripts and plays for children. At present she works as a librarian in Dubai. "Surprise" was first published in 1986 in *Kullna, Kullna Kullna nahibb al Bahr* by the Union of Writers of the United Arab Emirates (Sharjah, 1986), and Sara al Nawwaf's first collection of short stories was due to be published in late 1992.

Christina Pribichevich-Zoric was born in the United States but lived in Belgrade for twenty years after marrying a Yugoslav. She translated Milorad Pavic's award-winning *Dictionary of the Khazars*, and his much acclaimed *Landscape Painted with Tea* (both published by Hamish Hamilton). She has also translated Pavic's latest book, *The Inner Side of the Wind*, recently published in America by Alfred Knopf.

James Purdy was born in 1923 and grew up in rural Ohio, the setting for his 1960 novel, *The Nephew*. His first novel, *63: Dream Palace*, was published in England in 1957 to great praise, and his other works include *Malcolm*, *Mourners Below* and *On Glory's Course*. His most recent novel is *Out with the Stars*, published here by Peter Owen in 1992.

Phillip Ramey is an American composer, pianist and writer. His output encompasses orchestral and chamber pieces, and his most recent works are *Concerto No. 3 for Piano and Orchestra* and *Tangier Portraits for Piano*. Since 1977 he has been the annotator and programme editor of the New York Philharmonic Orchestra. This appreciation of Paul Bowles is taken from *Paul Bowles by his Friends*, edited by Gary Pulsifer (Peter Owen, 1992),an affectionate birthday tribute to the author.

Nawal el-Saadawi is one of the few Arabic women writers whose work has been widely published in the west. She founded the Arab Women's Solidarity Association and has written novels, stories, plays and social studies on the Egyptian community. Her work - and her life - has not always found favour with the authorities. "The Veil" was first published in Cairo in 1980, and reprinted in *Egyptian Tales and Short Stories*, edited by W.M.Hutchins (The American University in Cairo Press, 1987).

Mohammed Salmawy was born in 1945, received a B.A. in English Literature from Cairo University, two diplomas from Oxford and Birmingham Universities in Shakespeare and Modern English Literature, and his M.A. in Mass Communication from the American University in Cairo. He has written short stories, novels, television scripts and award-winning plays. "A Concerto for the Nay" was originally published in *al-Ahram* newspaper in 1984, reprinted in *Cairo Today* and again in *Egyptian Tales and Short Stories*, edited by W.M.Hutchins (The American University in Cairo Press, 1987).

Agnes Stein is a poet and translator, whose translation of a story by German writer Günter Kunert appeared in *Passport 3*. She is translating Herta Müller's first published collection of fiction, *Niederungen*.